SOIL GEOGRAPHY

by

J. G. CRUICKSHANK

Lecturer in Geography,
The Queen's University, Belfast

DAVID & CHARLES : NEWTON ABBOT

ISBN 0 7153 5157 5

COPYRIGHT NOTICE

Set in 10 on 12 pt Plantin
and printed in Great Britain
by Latimer Trend & Company Limited Plymouth
for David & Charles (Publishers) Limited
South Devon House   Newton Abbot   Devon

Contents

List of Illustrations

LINE FIGURES IN TEXT

Preface

THIS TEXTBOOK DOES NOT ATTEMPT TO TAKE THE READER TO THE FRONTIERS OF pedological research, but aims only to be an introduction to soil geography. Thus, I have drawn freely on published material to set out for the reader the most widely accepted ideas and explanations in soil geography. In many places I have tried to demonstrate the changing interpretation of soils and soil phenomena, providing previously held ideas and terms along with those currently creditable. Knowing the present interpretation of processes is always one of the real concerns of the student. The text is intended to be for geographers, geologists, biologists and agriculturalists in the early stages of a university or college training, and particular attention has been given to communicating information in a discursive style in the hope that it may encourage some to read further in the subject.

I have attempted to cover a wider range of topics than might be expected in a 'Soil geography', and as a result I have reduced the length of discussions on some familiar topics. Some readers may be disappointed with the brief mention given to such important matters as weathering, soil moisture, and soil erosion, but detailed consideration of these is given in published texts readily available to geographers and geologists. Instead, I have devoted extra space to the discussion of soil as an organic medium and as a resource, since I feel these are neglected topics in soil geography. Some practical advice on field work, laboratory tests, and soil map use is provided in the last chapter which is also an innovation of a kind. Readers will notice that I have used podsol as a preferred spelling to the more common podzol, and felspar for feldspar.

It will be clear to friends and former students that I have presented here a revision of pedology lectures given by me in the Department of Geography in The Queen's University of Belfast over the past ten years. For this long preparation, I owe gratitude to many who have taught, trained, and stimulated me in soil geography at the University of Aberdeen, at the Macaulay Institute for Soil Research in Aberdeen, and at Queen's. Two visits to Canada for professional work have further extended my experience and interest in soil geography, as have shorter visits to Denmark, Iceland, and Greenland. Without any doubt, a teacher owes the greatest debt of all to his students whose reaction is the most powerful influence on his teaching.

This book has become a singularly personal project for me, and I must accept full responsibility for all the subject matter and interpretations it contains. Most of the photographs and some of the drawings are also my own work! However, I would like to take this opportunity to thank Dr Nicholas Stephens and Mr Cyril Bown who, in personal capacities as long-standing friends, offered constructive criticism after reading drafts of the text. Also, I would like to thank my friends Dr David B. Prior, Dr Nicholas Stephens, Dr Conrad E. Heidenreich, and Mr Brian Kerr for giving me permission to reproduce their photographs from tropical and other lands. Miss Eileen Duncan and Mr Randal Nelson, Department of Geography, Queen's University of Belfast, provided a great deal of assistance with the cartography. The maps and line drawings have been redrawn from published sources, and I hope I have fully recognised the origin of the material.

Finally, I must thank Margaret M. Bower who has given me invaluable and immeasurable assistance with field work, library consultation, criticism of literary style, proofreading, indexing, and who is also incidentally my wife!

April 1972
Department of Geography
The Queen's University
Belfast

CHAPTER ONE

Soil as a Concept

EVER SINCE MAN BECAME A FARMER, HE HAS BEEN INTERESTED IN AND DEPENDENT
on soil. In particular, man, as a farmer, has been concerned with the wider and
more productive use of soil, achieved only by increasing his understanding of
this medium and its formation. For the millennia of time this understanding
of soil has been derived from the practical experience of farming, by trial and
error methods. In many parts of the world this is still the basis of soil knowledge despite the progress of 'western' technology, and even in parts of the
developed countries there are still farmers who trust folklore more than trained
government agricultural advisors. This concept of soil as a useful and productive medium for man's crops, developed in the chapter 'Soil as a Resource', is
only one view of soil, albeit the oldest and the most lasting. Any scientific
appraisal of the concept of soil should include a wider review of ideas, explanations, and hypotheses about soil formation that have been advanced at different
periods in time and at different levels of understanding. The history of pedological thought can be presented as a chronological outline of the development
of research and theory about soil formation, from which emerge finally various
classifications of soil units.

The distribution of early settlement was apparently influenced by soil type
and site conditions. For instance, the primitive cultivation methods of Neolithic times in the British Isles meant that man was attracted to the well-
drained and most workable soils. Good drainage carried with it the disadvantage of leaching or the chemical exhaustion of these soils, so that a shifting of
settlement and cultivation was necessary if the community was dependent
solely on tillage. In Western Europe, later prehistoric farming relied heavily
on animal husbandry which both supplemented and supported crop cultivation, allowing a partially sedentary organisation. In the tropics and in the

Americas, farming communities depended less on stock and usually were forced to move camp once all the soil within a half-day's walking distance had been exhausted by cropping. Although this information has not been specifically recorded by the societies themselves, archaeological evidence has revealed that degrees of permanence in prehistoric settlements were related to their agricultural organisation and to the character of local soils, the initial choice of settlement site being much influenced by the latter.

In historic times, man's awareness of soil conditions has been recorded since the literature of Classical Greece and Rome. Hippocrates, Theophrastus, Herodotus, Varro, Lucretius, and Virgil are among many who have referred to soil in general texts about the nature of the universe, travels, and exploration of the earth. Soil was regarded as the medium which supported plant life. It was crudely classified by the visible properties of the cultivated surface, such as the colour, texture, and stoniness. The depth of the soil was often reported, and this along with any other property of soil was viewed as a condition for plant growth. The Greeks also first expounded the idea that soil or earth was one of the four components of all matter—fire, water, earth, and air—and consequently soil was ranked as a basic element even if shrouded in a certain amount of mystery. These relatively simple, vague and yet obvious concepts of soil had little scientific foundation, but survived as frequently quoted statements until the new scientific concepts of the nineteenth century.

Even at the period of agricultural improvement in Western Europe, as late as the early nineteenth century, soil was being described in terms of the texture of its cultivated surface. In the county volumes for England published by the Board of Agriculture between 1790 and 1810, maps depict the soils of the county as soil regions of rich loam, wet clay, poor sand, etc (see page 17). The information was very general, restricted to top soil and intended as a crude guide to the agricultural potential of the district. It is curious that so little attention was given to soil mapping and that there was no significant advance in understanding soil processes in an age of agricultural improvement, but most of the effort seems to have gone into re-shaping field systems and the physical reorganisation of agricultural communities. In a number of countries in Western Europe, the extension and enclosure of the agricultural area in the early nineteenth century necessitated new land valuations. In many cases, the undertaking was massive and hurried, resulting in variation due to operational error by the surveyor as well as to soil conditions! In Britain and Ireland at least, there was no constructive by-product from these surveys in the form of a contribution to soil knowledge. The opportunity had been there, and a similar situation half a century later in Russia was seized by Dokuchaev to establish pedology as an independent discipline.

Pedology as a scientific discipline is still a youthful member of the natural sciences. It is the study of the morphology and distribution of soils in the places where they have formed. It belongs to the older and more embracing discipline of soil science, the other member parts of which had beginnings a little before and also after that of pedology. In this discussion we are not concerned with the foundation or the history of soil chemistry, soil physics, soil microbiology, soil mineralogy, and other member parts of soil science, but rather with the inception and growth of pedology within the last century. To do this, we must look first and principally to the Russians who formed a school of pedologists at St Petersburg (Leningrad) in the late nineteenth century under Dokuchaev. From this beginning in 1872 in the geological laboratory at St Petersburg University, Dokuchaev went on to explore pedogenesis and the Russian pedologists, in their geographical and linguistic isolation, became pre-eminent in the methodology of pedology until well into the present century. At first their ideas only filtered, and after 1914 spread westward; while they were modified and developed by many, particularly by Marbut and other Americans, they were never refuted. These two greatest names in the history of pedo-logical thought, Dokuchaev and Marbut, were also men of acute geographical awareness and indeed should be regarded as geographers. Dokuchaev's geo-graphical appreciation played a critical part in the formulation of the first theories of pedogenesis during his land valuation survey of Nizhnii Novgorod province, and the same was true for Marbut's ideas on soil mapping and soil classification. After all, these are exercises that are based on the synthesis of the elements of the natural environment which is the primary skill of the physical geographer. Much of Dokuchaev's writing was concerned with the unity and integration of the natural environment, and from this background—so similar in word and concept to that of Darwin for his *Origin of Species*— came the theory of pedogenesis proposing that soil was an independent natural

body, the product of the interaction of all the elements of the natural environment. Dokuchaev's connection with Darwin was more than fortuitous, because
in the philosophy of both the evolutionary element is essential. Soil was regarded as an organism in the sense that the passing of time witnessed changes
in its form and function. Soil was a dynamic creation of the natural environment,
reflecting changes in the character of its soil-forming elements. These theories,
along with a wealth of new terminology, emanated from Dokuchaev and his
associates, but before considering the Russian school of pedology in detail we
must examine earlier searching for an understanding of soil formation.

Nineteenth century pedological thought before Dokuchaev. The
foundations for pedological hypotheses were being laid in the century (1780–
1880) before Dokuchaev, and were by-products of research in soil fertility
connected with the period of agricultural improvement and advances in
chemistry in Western Europe. The best-known names were those of German
scientists although there were also important contributions from workers in
Britain and Scandinavia. The German A. D. Thaer, around 1809, supported
by Davy in Britain and Wallerius and Berzelius in Sweden, championed the
widely held theory of the early decades of the nineteenth century that plants
fed directly on the decaying organic matter or, as Thaer proposed, 'humus' of
the soil. Grassland and other humus-rich soils were considered the most fertile
and every effort was made to maintain the organic levels by applying manure.
In 1843, Julius von Liebig published his ideas that plants absorbed only mineral
substances from the soil. Liebig proved to be a profound influence on other
German soil scientists, and collectively they were responsible for the so-called
'agro-geology' school which postulated a geological origin for soil. German
geologists were attracted to the study of soil, and one of them, Albert Fallou
(1794–1877), was even regarded by some as the founder of pedology. Although
Fallou defined soil as a distinct formation, he stressed its geological derivation
and showed no understanding of the complex of soil-forming factors, later
demonstrated by the Russians. A further distinction differentiating soil from
weathered rock was made subsequently by another German, Emil Ramann
(1851–1926), but nevertheless the view of soil science as soil geology prevailed
for the rest of the nineteenth century in Western Europe and America. The
publications of N. S. Shaler and E. W. Hilgard in the United States between

> The soil map of the county of Suffolk, pre-
> pared for the Board of Agriculture county
> report in 1797. Note that the soils are
> mapped according to topsoil structure—
> sand, stony, and rich loam—and not by
> genetic type

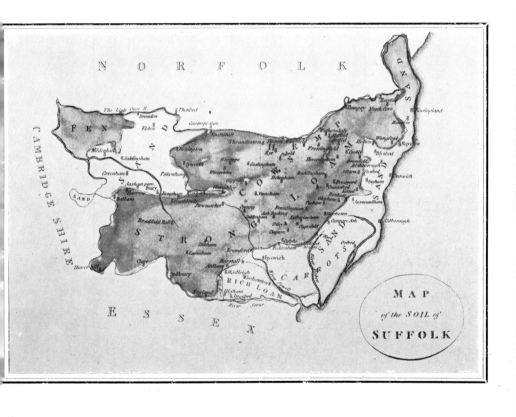

MAP
of the SOIL of
SUFFOLK

1860 and 1906, and J. R. Kilroe's *Soil-Geology of Ireland* in 1907, are a few examples of the general acceptance of the geological origin of soils in the period before the translation of Russian soil literature.

Ramann may be regarded as the transitional figure between the soil geologists and the pedologists. He made early contact with Russian pedologists and was well informed about their research before the end of the nineteenth century. Ramann was an early contributor to *Soviet Soil Science* (formerly *Pochvovedeniye*) within the first two or three years of its introduction in 1899. Despite that, his publications do not reveal much influence from the Russians, and he remained a soil geologist interested in relating soil with climatic regions. For most of his professional life Ramann was professor of soil science and agricultural chemistry at Munich, and his main experimental work was on forest soils. His classification of world soils was based on climatic regions, and he regarded the influence of climate as the starting point in understanding soil formation.

The Russian school of pedology. There are a number of recognised 'schools' of pedology that have made a reputation by their achievement in soil research, soil survey, and soil classification. The oldest and probably most respected is that of the Russians, certainly without rival in the first half of the past century. It was responsible for the first theory of soil formation that has survived the test of time and developed successfully. The now widely accepted ideas that soil is a complex independent material produced by a number of processes were not found in a moment of inspiration, but were worked out slowly by the Russians over at least two decades and followed by many subsequent modifications. In some cases these came from workers in other parts of Europe but were incorporated in the evolving Russian soil philosophy, which had the protection of language isolation in its early years. Additionally there was the stimulus of the demand for more soil knowledge in the agricultural colonisation and expansion through the Russian grasslands in the late nineteenth century, necessitating a massive survey and a considerable number of soil surveyors. Several of these became internationally known pedologists, and the most eminent of the nineteenth century were Vasilii Dokuchaev (1846–1903), Nikolai Sibirtzev (1860–99), and P. A. Kostychev (1845–95). Dokuchaev is perhaps the greatest name in pedology, because he was the first, became the

The A B C sequence of soil horizons as arranged by Dokuchaev in the 1880s. At this time, the B horizon was interpreted simply as a transitional horizon between the A and C; only later was it understood to be an illuvial horizon

B

leader and founder of the Russian school, and was something of a philosopher and romantic as well as a great scientist. It is worth while devoting special attention to him as he established the style and the conceptual framework of Russian pedology.

Vasilii Dokuchaev was intended for the priesthood, but altered his course while at St Petersburg University in time to graduate in natural science. His first professional post was curator of the geological laboratory at the university from 1872, and this work brought him in contact with the study of soils. There existed in Russia at that time what was called the 'True Society of Economics' which became concerned with the need to increase agricultural productivity in the Russian grasslands. On their behalf, Dokuchaev was asked to undertake four years' research from 1877 to 1881 on a geologic-geographical survey of the European steppe-lands, on which he based his *Russian Chernozem* published in 1883. In this pioneer work, Dokuchaev proposed that soils had an origin of their own and that the 'chernozem' soil of the grasslands was provided by both vegetation and mineral materials. In 1882 Dokuchaev and several assistants began another four-year agricultural valuation and land capability survey, this time in the province of Gork'iy (then Nizhnii-Novgorod) 200 miles east of Moscow. The work was organised as a comparative geography of various regions to embrace all the elements of the physical environment, and included both soil and land valuation surveys. Similar surveys had taken place in other European countries earlier in the nineteenth century, but probably the inexperience of the assessors and their pre-dating of German work on soil chemistry inhibited any pedological breakthrough. It was in the first of the fourteen volumes of his *Data on Land Appraisal in Nizhnii-Novgorod Province* (published in 1886) that Dokuchaev proposed an elementary classification of natural or *normal soils,* consequently coining some of the most familiar soil profile names, such as chernozem, solonchak, sierozem, and podsol. More than that, he created a philosophy 'concerned with the numerous, multiform relations and interactions . . . which exist between . . . rocks, geomorphology, soils, surface and ground water, local climate, flora, fauna and man'. Dokuchaev believed that soil was one of a number of natural bodies that expressed themselves variably both in space and time, saying that soils 'are not only very variable values in space, but also in certain respects comparatively unstable in time'. He is also quoted as saying, 'As any other natural body, soil has its past, its life and its genesis.' Dokuchaev was following earlier naturalist-geographers such as Humboldt and Darwin, and geologists like Lyell and Hutton in his pre-occupation with the organised unity of all natural bodies and their dynamic quality of gradual evolution. He followed the school of uniformitarianism or actualism in geology and was simply proposing an evolutionary framework for a related science. Dokuchaev had been trained as a geologist and was un-doubtedly influenced by earlier geologists and biologists in his statements on soil evolution, yet for soil formation processes he proposed a much wider spectrum of interaction to include all elements of the natural environment. It is well known that Dokuchaev attached primary importance to climate as a soil-forming factor and classified his 'normal soils' by regional climatic type; nevertheless he considered the role of plants and animal organisms of almost equal importance. Soil was considered a biological formation and unless it contained organic life in some form, it lost its distinctiveness as soil.

Dokuchaev was the pioneer, leader, and philosopher of the Russian school of pedology, but left most of the work of field study, analysis, and soil classi-fication to his assistants. It was Sibirtzev who was mainly responsible for the first comprehensive classification of soils—one of many genetic classifications from the Russians—presented at the 7th International Geological Congress in 1897 and in his textbook *Soil Science* in 1899. In this, soils are categorised as zonal, which had been the normal soils of Dokuchaev, intra-zonal, and azonal according to their degree of dependence on climate as a soil former. *Pochvo-vedeniye* (*Soviet Soil Science*) was launched in 1899 as the first such journal of the discipline, and by the end of the century the pre-eminence of Russians in pedology seemed assured. However, they had not succeeded in this achieve-ment entirely unaided, having borrowed from P. E. Müller of Denmark in the 1890s a vital link in their understanding of soil development. Hitherto, the Russians had been considering only the surface so-called A horizons in their description and classification of soils, but Müller provided evidence to asso-ciate the lower B horizons of podsols with the rest of the soil profile. It was not until well into the twentieth century in the publications of Konstantin Glinka (1867–1927) that the Russians accepted the full A, B, C horizon designations within soil profiles, and they were not used with complete confidence until the Second International Congress of Soil Science held in 1932. (See page 158.)

Conceptually, Russian pedology has become fossilised in the past half-century and its soil classification theory is still based on the genetic framework adopted in the pioneering stage. Basinski (1959) has reviewed the evolution of Russian soil classification in four stages: (a) the geographic-environmental classifications of Dokuchaev and Sibirtzev (1890–1900), (b) factorial classifications of Glinka and others based on the interaction of more than one soil-forming factor (1900–30), (c) soil process and degree of process classifications (1910–30) and (d) evolutionary classifications based on a single soil-forming process with geographical variation (1935–60, but modified recently). The Russians are now more respected for their encyclopaedic soil literature and the massive scale of their soil investigation and mapping than for any recent contribution to soil classification. Their achievement is almost a century of distinctive pedological philosophy which has helped to establish the discipline of soil science so firmly in their country.

Pedological thought in Europe. It is more difficult to generalise about the pedology of the rest of the Europeans as, compared with the Americans and the Russians, they have no strongly developed schools of pedology. Some of the most outstanding individuals who have contributed through personal research did not try to establish soil surveys or university disciplines in their countries. Where some kind of pedological organisation was established, the emphasis usually has been less directed to agriculture than in Russia or the United States and perhaps for that reason has received less official government support in the countries concerned.

In Denmark, the pedological work of P. E. Müller (1840–1926) was ancillary to his research for the Danish Heath Society's programme of agricultural reclamation and reafforestation from 1866 onward. In the 1880s Müller investigated and named the *mor, moder,* and *mull* types of soil surface organic horizons under beech woodland, and was the first man satisfactorily to explain the formation of podsol soil profiles following his research on compacted sub-surface B horizons. The work of the Danish Heath Society has expanded and diversified over the last century, but it has not included soil survey. Müller left no other organisational legacy, although in Denmark research has continued in particular problems of soil chemistry. Emil Ramann has been mentioned already as a contemporary of Müller who also made significant contributions in soil chemistry. In Germany or Austria, Ramann had no successors of equal stature until Kubiena after World War II. He was particularly concerned with the search to find a natural basis for the classification of soils, as is expressed in his book *Soils of Europe* published in 1953. Between the two World Wars, pedological research was almost dormant in continental Europe, and certainly lagged far behind that of the Americans and Russians until the post-World War II period.

In Britain, the Rothamsted Experimental Station for soil research was founded in 1843, and in Scotland, the Macaulay Institute at Aberdeen in 1930. Both acted as headquarters for all types of soil research and as bases for their respective national soil surveys: from 1939 for the survey of England and Wales, and from 1946 for Scotland. Soil survey in Great Britain dates from as far back as 1911 when the first of a number of county and special surveys were published. These became more commonly produced in the 1920s and 1930s as contract surveys for specific agricultural purposes. Some of the later private surveys have survived the test of time very well (Kay, 1934), and introduced soil terms and definitions adopted later by the national soil surveys. The latter, in contrast with many other national surveys, have not been known for applied work, but rather for inventory soil mapping and description. Senior members of the national soil surveys such as G. W. Robinson (1932) and B. W. Avery (1956) have been responsible for soil classifications which developed from the work of soil survey in Britain. Alex Muir, director of the Soil Survey of England and Wales from 1946 to 1962, was one of the most influential pedologists in Britain, gathering some of his experience directly from personal contact with the Russians in the 1930s. The *Journal of Soil Science* was not established in Britain until 1949.

In the Netherlands, a very active soil survey organisation has concentrated on detailed and rather specialised types of soil mapping in response to the agricultural problems of reclaiming land. Their work is an outstanding example of the application of soil survey to man's colonisation of the land. France is notable as a country still without a national soil survey and yet has produced outstanding pedologists like Oudin, Aubert, and Duchaufour. These men and

many others, who have been responsible for selective soil mapping in countries like France, Belgium, Spain, Portugal, Germany and Yugoslavia, have a
history of soil research behind them going back to the nineteenth century, the
last twenty-five years being most productive in pedological investigation. The
same must be said of countries like Ireland, Iceland, Italy, Cyprus, Turkey,
Switzerland and Greece, which began their organised soil survey and pedological
research in the post-World War II period. The *Soil Map of Europe*, with its
explanatory text, published by FAO in 1966, provided an excellent review of
the state of pedology in European countries at that time. As part of Europe's
contribution, the soil classifications of individual European pedologists such
as Duchaufour, Kubiena, Robinson, Avery and FitzPatrick are of great international importance and will be considered later in Chapter 5 on soil classification.

The American school of pedology. Soil survey organisations have been
established in most countries in all continents as part of the post-World War II
expansion of environmental research. In the English language, the distinctive
achievements in soil survey and environmental assessment of the Canadians,
Australians and New Zealanders merit international recognition. In Canada,
soil survey has been organised on a provincial basis; most of the agricultural
land in all provinces has been surveyed at a reconnaissance level. The Australians have integrated soil research with other landscape studies and produced
land system units as well as soil mapping units. However, in the history of
pedological thought only the Americans can rival the Russians in the length of
time and scale of undertaking in pedological research and philosophy.

The Americans can almost match the Russians for the early dates of adoption
of pedological ideas, but did not pioneer, to the same degree, research into
pedogenic processes. Hilgard, Shaler and Whitney had published the results
of soil surveys between 1860 and 1900. The US Soil Survey was established
under Whitney's direction in 1898, and the bald facts seem to bear close comparison with Russian progress by the end of the nineteenth century. There
were major differences between their respective concepts of soil, but it is remarkable that both had started their pedological interest about the same time
while in complete isolation from each other. The Russians did have a soils
exhibit, reporting progress to date, at the World's Columbian Exposition at

Chicago in 1893, but it seemed to pass almost unnoticed by pedologists in America. Ramann and others in Europe were aware of Russian interpretations by the end of the century, but widespread interest was not roused until after 1914. The man responsible for communicating the new ideas in the United States was C. F. Marbut (1863–1935) who became one of the best known names in world pedology as well as founder of the American school.

C. F. Marbut's contribution to pedology is of particular interest for geographers, because he himself was a geographer—partly by training and certainly in attitude. He was born in a rural community in Missouri in 1863, and after a considerable struggle to receive school education finally reached the University of Missouri at the age of 22 years. He studied geology and later went on to graduate school at Harvard (1893–95). There he was a student of N. S. Shaler—who had published his *Origin and nature of soils* in 1890—and also of W. M. Davis. Marbut's interest in soils can be traced to this contact at Harvard, but whether his future work was influenced by the philosophy of W. M. Davis at the time is doubtful. The two did remain in contact and had great mutual respect for each other, but another thirty years had to pass before Marbut incorporated Davisian ideas into soil interpretation. The 1890s was an exciting period to have been at graduate school in the United States, and later ideas from Marbut make it tempting to suggest influence from the studies of Cowles at Chicago and Davis at Harvard, clarifying the dynamic character of natural phenomena. Marbut left Harvard to become a field and academic geologist in his home state of Missouri, helping to establish a soil survey there and being responsible for publishing a soil map of Missouri in 1904. In the same year Marbut contributed to the foundation meeting of the Association of American Geographers, of which he became President in 1924, and also met at the first conference another cycle-of-erosion geomorphologist, A. Penck. When Marbut was appointed consultant scientist with the US Soil Survey in 1910, and even when its 'scientist in charge' or director in 1913, his view of soils was that of a geologist-geographer in the style of most pedologists outside Russia. Soils were considered to be associated with the rock types, to which, it was said, they owed their origin; and sometimes also they were associated with geologic-geomorphologic provinces.

The soil science of university courses and research institutes in Russia was first reported at length in a foreign language in the German translation of a book by Glinka—*Die Typen der Bodenbildung*—in 1914. This was the text that impressed Marbut so much that he undertook the English translation in the following years and adopted Russian terms and concepts into the work of the United States soil survey. By the time that the first International Congress of Soil Science had been held in 1927 in America (organised by Marbut), the English-speaking world knew Russian pedology both from the Marbut translation and from Russian papers given at the congress. The journal *Soil Science* was introduced in 1916 from Rutgers College, to be followed in 1936 by the *Proceedings of the Soil Science Society of America*—the most important soil journals outside Russia before World War II. Russian theory and terminology was being discussed also in this pre-war period at the second International Congress of Soil Science in Russia in 1932 and at the third in England (Oxford) in 1935. Marbut died in that year while in China on a post-congress tour. He had achieved an international reputation, and in his own country was recognised as an outstanding teacher and communicator of the new concepts of pedology. He had lectured annually from 1922 on soil geography at Clark University and had directed and inspired the soil survey of America, being responsible in particular for the 'Soils of the United States' section in the *Atlas of American Agriculture* (1935) and for his classification of soils. Marbut was honoured as a geographer on several occasions, and he was always concerned with the geographical contributions to, and applications of, soil survey in America.

The first director of the United States soil survey had been Milton Whitney, and because he attached great importance to texture (particle size composition) as a soil property the texture of the soil surface was systematically observed and recorded as a distinguishing characteristic of *soil type* in the early years of the US survey. In 1904 the *soil series* was introduced to include all soil types developed on the same parent material (current definition on page 29). By 1913, when Marbut became 'scientist in charge', the soil survey had identified 550 soil series, by 1930 about 1,400, by 1938 some 2,000, and currently nearly 9,000. This dramatic increase has been made possible by narrowing the permitted ranges of characteristics as more information has become available, as well as by extending the mapping area of the survey. The soil series was regarded as the primary unit of soil mapping and the basis for correlation from one part of the country to another. During Marbut's time, the concept of this primary unit changed from being a geological unit to a mainly climatically developed unit and ultimately to an independent natural unit defined on the basis of its own properties. At Marbut's death in 1935 the world was on the eve of war, and the break conveniently marks an end to the pioneer phase in pedological research.

In the post-World War II period, American pedologists both in the soil survey and in the universities have taken over international leadership in soil nomenclature and classification. The *US Soil Survey Manual* (1951) was a major publication, revised several times subsequently, which governs methods of field survey and defines terminology. In conception, the soil is now viewed as a three-dimensional body and interpreted functionally as a type of 'open system' through which there is a continuing flow of energy. Before we consider the dynamic and three-dimensional character of soil in detail (this follows in the next two chapters), it is appropriate at this stage formally to introduce and define soil for the reader.

An introduction to soil and soil terminology. Soil is a material with which everyone is familiar. It is commonplace; it surrounds us, and can be identified as easily by the layman as by the farmer. Most people recognise variation in the appearance of soil over space, or in other words that different types of soil exist in different places, even if they cannot explain why. Soil in one place also changes its characteristics with the passing of time, but the time interval for noticeable change is greater than the human mind can register, and usually greater even than a human lifetime. Perhaps this is the reason why man's curiosity about soil changes is so reluctantly aroused, and why soil continues to be one of the most seen and yet least understood natural phenomena surrounding man. The changing concept of soil is important enough to be considered elsewhere in this text (see particularly Chapter 5), but that discussion refers to progress made at the frontiers of pedological or soil research. For most people living now, the idea of soil is little changed from that of prehistoric man—simply, a substance in which plants will grow. Surprisingly enough, this is still a satisfactory definition of soil. Soil is any material in which plants will grow, whether they do or not. Where plants are found, soil contains its own internal biological life and is more complete as a soil. Naturally there is a great deal of soil on the surface of the earth which does not support plant life because the environment above the soil does not meet plant requirements for growth. This does not defeat the definition of soil as it is possible to find potential soil without plant life in deserts, on mountain tops, in polar regions, and below lakes or rivers. This definition of soil is simple and limited, taking account only of its properties as a plant rooting medium. Far more significant in pure scientific investigation are soil properties and characteristics produced by internal soil processes which are influenced by soil parent material and the topography as well as by extraneous elements of the natural environment such as climate. This aspect of soil, its pedological character, is that which is most variable over time and space, and because of this we may think of soil as a dynamic medium.

As an introduction and only as an outline for later discussion, some of the basic soil terms and units will be defined. Although the soil body or soil mantle obviously has a three-dimensional form, it has been represented traditionally by a so-called 'two-dimensional' section or slice called the *soil profile*. In fact, any section or profile through soil must have a third dimension of thickness wherever stones or structural units are encountered. Although the third dimension has never been included in the definition of a soil profile, it has been implicit in the practical use of the concept. The horizontal sub-divisions of this soil profile are its *horizons*; they look like depositional layers, but have been differentiated by processes producing internal soil redistribution. Horizons are an expression of pedogenesis although they are not necessarily related to the current stage of pedogenesis reached in the development of a particular soil. They may be inherited from processes no longer operative. Sometimes the soil profile is accepted as the basic unit of soil study. However, the soil body in the field is three-dimensional, so it is more realistic to consider a three-dimensional volumetric unit, called a *pedon*, as the basic soil unit. It is the smallest field unit that can be isolated for inspection. The pedon requires to have all the horizons of a vertical section present within its boundaries which are usually more difficult to delimit laterally or areally than the vertical boundaries of horizons. A number of pedons together, such as comprise a field mapping unit, are collectively called a *polypedon*. A pedon is usually less than 10 m², but a polypedon

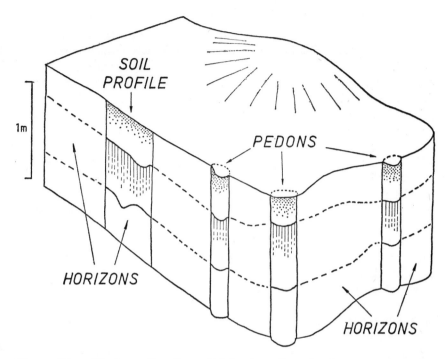

Fig 1:1   The soil body or soil medium which is a three-dimensional cover over most of
the earth's surface. It is differentiated by pedogenic processes into soil layers called
horizons. These are present in both vertical sections (soil profiles) and cores or
columns (pedons) through the soil mantle. In glaciated high-latitude landscapes, soil
is usually about one metre thick, but is more and less in other environments

is large enough to be outlined on a field map and nearly corresponds to what is
known as a *soil series* mapping unit. A soil series is a composite unit, but being
the basic unit of soil mapping it is expected to be predominantly composed of
one named soil profile type and confined to one parent material. These soil
terms will be more fully discussed and applied in Chapters 4 and 8.

Pedology, as the study of the morphology and distribution of soils, is
essentially a field science which depends on certain laboratory techniques to

provide supplementary information to aid field interpretation. Pedology is, by this definition, very close to soil geography except that the latter is concerned with all kinds of distributions involving soil, from those of natural genesis to limitations for soil cultivation. Pedology is less concerned with distributions and more with the morphological expression of pedogenesis and the complex development of the three-dimensional soil mantle.

The development of pedological thought has been discussed; here the point being emphasised is that pedology is only a part of the whole of soil science, but is the part most closely related to geography. It is the study of pedogenesis, or soil evolution, and the distribution or spatial variation of pedogenesis. Soil geography is different only by being perhaps less technical, less specific and broader in scope, necessarily being a spatial study of both natural and man-modified soils. Being concerned with soil distributions, soil geography must also take account of the spatial variation in the environmental elements that interact to form soil and this is the theme of the next chapter. The soil-forming environment which includes topography and landforms, rock and superficial deposits, climate and vegetation, is incorporated in the content of other geographical specialisms as all its constituents are spatially variable. Efforts made by geographers and others to explain the soil-forming role and spatial variation of those components of the natural environment form contributory studies for soil geography. To sum up, soil geography is largely the study of the spatial variation of the interaction of environmental elements; and this is how soil is made.

Bibliography

AVERY, B. W. A classification of British soils, *6th International Congress of Soil Science*, E (1956), 279–85.

BASINSKI, J. J. The Russian approach to soil classification and its recent development, *Journal of Soil Science*, 10, No 1 (1959), 14–26.

JOFFE, J. S. *Pedology*, New Jersey, Pedology Publications, 1949.

KAY, F. F. A soil survey of the eastern portion of the Vale of the White Horse, *Bull. Fac. Agric. Hort., Univ. of Reading*, No 48, 1934.

KUBIENA, W. L. *The soils of Europe*, Murby, London, 1953.

NIKIFOROFF, C. C. Re-appraisal of the soil, *Science*, 129 (1959), 186–96.

ROBINSON, G. W. *Soils, their origin, constitution and classification*, Murby, London, 1932.

RUSSELL, J. E. The rebirth of soil science in Great Britain, *Soil Science*, 94 (1962), 204–13.

SIMONSON, R. W. Concept of soil, *Advances in Agronomy*, 20 (1968), 1–47.

SOIL SCIENCE SOCIETY OF AMERICA. *Life and work of C. F. Marbut*, Columbia, Missouri, 1942.

SOIL SURVEY STAFF. *Soil Survey Manual*, US Department of Agriculture, Washington, pp 503, 1961.

CHAPTER TWO

Soil as a Dynamic Medium

SOIL IS OFTEN COMPARED WITH OTHER ORGANISMS. ALTHOUGH IT CANNOT reproduce and is not mobile, soil is a natural phenomenon with its own independent organisation, and is formed by the interaction of other natural elements. Soil is like an organism mainly because its characteristics are changed by natural processes; it is a dynamic medium. It develops in the sense that it evolves through stages until it reaches a slowly changing equilibrium with its formative environment. Soil is produced by the combined working of the soil-forming factors. These are:

a climate
b vegetation
c other biotic factors, mainly animal organisms including man
d parent material—rock or transported material
e relief, ie, topography or surface configuration.

Seen in this way, soil is a dependent variable on the interaction of these five independent or partially independent variables. The soil-forming factors are not mutually exclusive and do affect one another as well as the soil product. Soil can be regarded as the integral of these five environmental factors, within specified time limits. Increase of time taken for soil formation may well alter the product.

Since the foundation of pedology as a scientific discipline in the 1880s, pedologists have applied a mathematical expression, or an idea in algebraic notation, to this compound and complex process of soil formation. Dokuchaev first suggested the following equation about eighty years ago.

$$s = f(c, o, p)t^0$$

where s = soil, c = climate, o = organisms, p = parent materials, and t^0 = relative age. It was an equation intended to be symbolic rather than utilitarian, and should be regarded only as a conceptual model. Subsequently, several other pedologists such as Hilgard, Shaw and Jenny proposed modifications to this expression and all added relief to the soil-forming factors. Organisms may be sub-divided into flora (vegetation) and fauna. These should be added to the equation with r = relief, v = vegetation and o = animal organisms to produce the following:

$$s = f(c, v, o, p, r)t^0$$

Although the five soil-forming factors are not entirely independent of each other in controlling pedogenesis, they do operate on different and independent scales of effectiveness. Each one may be sub-divided into constituent parts and is, in fact, a compound or group factor influencing soil formation. Climate as a soil former is effective through precipitation, aridity, temperature regimes, and other more sophisticated indices of humidity. Vegetation affects soil formation through both the quantity and quality of living and decaying plants. Other organisms (micro-flora and all animals) are mainly responsible for the decay of surface organic matter, and the composition, size, and activity of their populations is influenced by soil micro-environmental conditions. Parent material may be classified by its primary mineral composition and degree of weathering in its initial state before pedogenesis. Relief includes the influence of slope and drainage affected by slope. Thus each of these soil-forming factors embraces distinctive phenomena the influence of which has to be measured on individual and independent scales. Plant matter cannot be measured in the same units as temperature, rainfall, slope, or primary minerals. Because there are so many kinds of soil-forming factors and so many separate scales of measurement of the different phenomena involved in soil formation, the integral of all the soil-forming factors produces an almost infinite number of possible soil individuals. Furthermore, the variation in the soil-forming factors operates over the two dimensions of time and space. Thus, the nearly infinite variety of soils that exist over the earth's soil mantle is always changing with time because each or all of the soil-forming factors may change with time.

It is difficult to comprehend or even to imagine such complex and often irregular rates of change with time among independently, or partially independently, variable soil-forming factors. Indeed, their variation over space at any one moment in time is sufficient for consideration in the first stage of inquiry. This in itself is highly complicated and defies prediction even by the computer. The problem is partly one of measurement and the fact that the influence of some soil-forming factors is not quantifiable. Of course, climatic data are amenable to quantification, as is slope and some other elements of the soil-forming environment, but it is almost impossible to evaluate precisely the influence of plants and other organisms, or even parent material, on the formation of soil. The fact that all five soil-forming factors are compound and can be sub-divided, makes each a collective rather than an individual influence. This multiplicity of parts within soil-forming factors increases the number of real variables affecting soil formation and increases the possible number of distinctive soils produced. And further, these member parts of the soil-forming 'group-factors' are spatially variable. For example, the annual period of plant growth, of organic decay, of weathering, the composition of the plant cover, the soil fauna or the parent material, altitude, angle of slope, and many other characteristics of the soil-forming environment, can all change over space, sometimes independently, as happens with the primary mineral composition of parent material, or dependently, as happens with soil fauna.

A final problem—it is not possible to classify the degree of dependence among or between two soil-forming factors over space as the dependence itself alters as the strength mixture of soil-forming factors changes. This is a change that is also time dependent. A plant cover at a mature stage of development is less affected by extraneous conditions than is a community of colonising plants and so achieves a less dependent status among the soil-forming factors. A study of the spatial variation of the soil-forming environment must, therefore, consider both the change in actual values of the soil-forming factors as well as the degree of dependence among and between them—the same variables which are regarded as independent in the soil formation equations introduced earlier!

Climate and soil formation. Climate was regarded as the principal and dominant soil-forming factor for the greater part of the short history of pedological thought. Consequently the view came to be almost inviolable and very little modification was accepted until the last two or three decades. Climate is still recognised as a major influence on several processes and stages of soil formation, but no longer as the central one around which all pedogenic processes and soil classifications must revolve. Climate is remarkable among the

Prismatic structure in calcareous clay at a site in Somerset, England (see page 57)

soil-forming factors for the way in which it is involved in the various processes of soil formation and destruction; it is perhaps more penetrating and more varied in its influence than any of the other factors, but is not dominant over them. Climate affects soil formation in at least four main ways which are: weathering of parent material, transportation of parent material if it has been moved, pedogenesis or development of features by internal soil processes, and lastly erosion or physical removal of the soil body. These topics will be discussed in the paragraphs that follow.

Weathering of rock (or some other type of parent material if it has been transported) involves both physical and chemical reactions that are controlled directly and indirectly by climate. Weathering is of course affected also by the composition of the mineral material being weathered, by plants and their litter which provide hydrogen-rich organic solutions, and by the circulation of groundwater. Physical weathering depends less on the presence of moisture than does chemical weathering, but both are influenced by temperature which makes their reactions possible. For physical weathering, a large temperature change over short periods is the critical climatic control and this is most effective on dry, exposed mineral surfaces. Thus, the most active physical weathering is associated with arid and semi-arid environments which lack a protective plant cover and experience a considerable diurnal temperature range. Physical weathering is also important in polar deserts where it is most active in the short spring and autumn. At these seasons, there are frequent changes of temperature across freezing point causing physical disintegration of rock by the expansion of moisture on freezing. In the polar deserts there is no weathering of either kind during the complete freeze of winter, and the most active physical weathering in spring and autumn is at exposed sites without an insulating cover of snow or vegetation. Temperature changes that create expansion and contraction of materials are most disruptive on rock where joints, fissures, and bedding planes can be attacked or weakly cemented crystals can be forced apart.

Chemical weathering is a compound process composed of a number of different types of chemical reaction, some of which require oxygen and most moisture, while all respond to changes in temperature. There is no common temperature range which is optimal for all types of chemical weathering; they

(*Above*) A strongly horizonated podsol underlying seventeenth century Huron Indian midden material in Southern Ontario, Canada. The podsol is the natural profile of a sand deposit, originally highly acid but currently alkaline in reaction due to the superimposed drainage of base-rich water

through the midden; (*below*) buried humic horizons in black indicate former slope surfaces in part of Southern Ontario, near Georgian Bay, where the instability of sandy soil was connected with Indian clearance and cultivation in the seventeenth century (see page 63)

C

behave independently in finding a favourable range, but most have the characteristic of increasing their rate of reaction with increase of temperature.
Usually temperatures over 10° C are necessary to start these chemical reactions
and they can double their rate of reaction with every 10° C rise in temperature
above that. As some moisture is present in the parent material even in arid
environments, *hydrolysis* involving the break-up of water molecules into hydrogen, H, ions and hydroxyl, OH, ions is the most common type of chemical
weathering. It is found wherever moisture is present and even takes place in
polar and hot deserts, although on a very limited scale. In hydrolysis, the OH^-
ions displace and combine with metallic ions from primary minerals and are
lost from the medium, while the H^+ ions combine with the residual silicates to
form various secondary minerals. These are clay minerals of various types,
derived from felspars, micas, etc, and they are discussed later. Chemical
weathering also includes the chemical reactions of *oxidation* involving the
addition of oxygen, *reduction* involving the removal of oxygen, *carbonation*
with the addition of carbonate ions from carbonic acid, *hydration* with the
addition of water molecules, and *solution* by which whole minerals are dissolved
in water. The products of the last two types of reaction are easily carried out
of the weathering medium whenever sufficient moisture is available.

Physical and chemical weathering change solid rock into unconsolidated
mineral material. Physical weathering has the function of providing a greatly
increased surface area on which chemical reactions take place. Although the
two main types of weathering are influenced by and limited by different climatic parameters, there is no rigid environmental separation on the areas of
their occurrence. Both physical and chemical weathering take place in all
environments, indeed wherever soil has developed, but it is reasonable to
qualify this generalisation by saying that chemical weathering reaches its
maximum in scale and rate in the humid tropics, and is least active in the hot
and polar deserts. The global distribution of the scale and rates of physical
weathering tends to be complementary.

On large parts of the earth's surface the present soil has developed from
material transported from another place, and not from weathering of the rock
below (ie *in situ*). The main agents of *transportation* are gravity, ice, wind, and
surface running water, the last three of which are components of the climatic

system. In many cases, these agents moved and deposited soil parent material at some distant time in the past; the age of transported deposits is highly variable, but almost certainly the movement came after a period of weathering at the original site. Gravity, ice, wind, and water transport previously weathered and unconsolidated material. Weathering will continue at the deposition site for as long as primary and secondary minerals remain to be weathered; it is only briefly interrupted while transportation takes place. Weathering and the transportation of material, both influenced by climate, combine to provide a medium in which pedogenic processes can be initiated. The soil deposit may be derived also from the eroded material of a well-weathered and mature soil, as often happens to tropical red soils. Fluvial erosion by rivers or sheet wash is the most important present form of transportation of material; the products of wind movement are more limited by circumstances and those moved by ice are generally much older (at least 20,000 years BP), most being associated with the Pleistocene glaciations. Although ice has the power to move boulders great distances and to include them in glacial till, the active part of soil parent materials is the small size particles (< 2 mm diameter) comprising the matrix of any transported deposit. The differences among types of transported deposit will be discussed under parent materials.

Part of the transportation of parent material is the initial erosion by ice, wind, and water, necessary to provide the unconsolidated material. Ice is by far the most powerful of the agents of erosion, and there is no natural or man-made protection that can survive its force. Enormous volumes of loose materials, rocks and boulders have been moved out of their source areas by ice sheets and glaciers; farmland and farmsteads in Iceland have also been overrun in recent centuries. Man is defenceless against ice, but fortunately there are only a few examples of recent destruction of agricultural or potentially useful land by moving ice. Of much greater danger to agriculturally valuable soil is erosion by wind and running water, but against these, protective measures can be success-ful. What is done is particular to each type of erosion as the mechanics of the respective processes are distinctive and different. One form of protection is the maintenance of a plant cover to avoid exposure to wind or running water. A complete plant cover gives protection from surface water by intercepting the fall of rain and allowing more than otherwise (up to 25 per cent of the total) to be evaporated back into the atmosphere. Also its physical presence reduces the rate of surface run-off, and thus the greater time available for infiltration results in less water being lost in surface run-off. In other words, vegetation and its associated organic litter act as a sponge in absorbing a large proportion of the surface moisture and as a barrier in impeding its progress over the soil surface. The influence of slope on fluvial erosion can be shown by the fact that an increase in the angle of slope accelerates the rate of erosion, if other factors are constant and the surface is not receiving protection from plant cover. The effect is particularly marked for slopes up to 10 degrees, a doubling of the angle of slope producing a doubling in rate of run-off. Cultivated land should be ploughed and planted parallel to the contours of the slope to reduce surface run-off which would increase by the absence of a plant cover when the soil is exposed for ploughing.

Most critical of all is the climatic factor, in particular the amount, intensity, and distribution of rainfall through the year. Intense (high volume per unit time) rainfall is likely to be the most destructive as it combines volume and velocity to weaken and disintegrate the aggregates of soil particles. Once the soil particles have been separated and are in a water-saturated medium, they are easily removed from the soil body by surface run-off. Wind does not have the same power to destroy soil aggregates, and as a transporting agent is restricted by particle size to those less than 0·1 mm in diameter— at least for material that is to be wind-borne great distances. Wind is particularly effective as an agent of erosion on dry, exposed mineral surfaces such as occur in deserts. Land under cultivation should be protected from wind by growing tree shelter-belts to break and divert the passage of wind, and also by keeping the soil covered by an organic mat or 'mulch', if not by plants. These are examples of the ways in which climatic elements operate as promoters and destroyers of the soil deposit. It is a relationship that is also affected by other environmental factors such as vegetation and relief so that the distribution of erosion phenomena is not solely controlled by climate.

Within the soil body itself, climate has a marked influence on *pedogenic processes*, particularly where the drainage of the soil is good. It may also, through excessive rainfall, contribute to and aggravate poorly drained conditions by saturation of the ground. Climate is likely to affect soil-forming processes, as distinct from weathering, by contributing water to the soil from precipitation. This water provides the soil solution for the physical translocation of soil particles (called *eluviation*) and the removal of dissolved chemical compounds (called *leaching*) down through the soil profile under freely draining conditions. The leaching effectiveness of the local climate is measured over a year as the amount of solution available in the soil to dissolve and carry leachable compounds from upper into lower horizons of the soil body. The leaching effectiveness in mainly humid or sub-humid climates has been defined by Arkley (1967) as the cumulative excess of precipitation over potential evapotranspiration through consecutive months of the moist season. In arid climates where most of the annual precipitation is likely to come within a short period and even in one storm, it has been found expedient to use the average precipitation of the wettest month in the year as an approximation of the moisture available for leaching. In practice, there is very little moisture available for leaching in arid climates and it usually comes from one or two rainstorms. The very short-term and short-distance leaching near the surface may be counterbalanced by an upward movement of salt solutions towards the (drier) surface of the soil during the long arid season. Even in humid environments with an extended moist season, an excess of moisture for soil leaching is usually available only during the moist cooler season as evapotranspiration will counterbalance it at other times. In these environments, with a complete, and often dense, vegetation cover, surface run-off is a small proportion of the total moisture in circulation and may be omitted from the water balance budget. The amount of water entering the soil is altered more by the character of the plant cover, colour and organic matter content of the top soil.

All soils have the capacity to hold moisture within their own fabric, and usually never completely dry out even under climatic drought. In extreme aridity, the moisture remaining in the soil will be held or stretched over the surface of the soil particles with the greatest surface tension force. However, the minimum moisture storage in the solum will be equivalent to between 10 and 15 cm water per unit area. In arid and semi-arid climates, it is found that the leaching effectiveness, taken as the mean precipitation of the wettest month, is much less in quantity than the minimal moisture storage and consequently has very little leaching impact, as it goes into storage to satisfy this first. At sites where the leaching effectiveness has been calculated at more than 45 cm moisture, which is much greater than the maximum moisture storage capacity of the soil, the leaching process will have made a clear and pronounced impression on soil development. Translocated compounds, moved from upper to lower zones in the soil under free drainage, give a distinctive character to soil horizons by their presence or absence. The soil composition can increase or reduce the effect of leaching from one parent material to another, and hence modifies the effect of climate.

As part of the role of climate in pedogenesis, its moisture and temperature components also affect the rate of decay and incorporation into the soil of surface organic litter. The decay is conducted by millions of plant micro-organisms (bacteria, fungi, and algae) as well as by lesser numbers of animal meso- and macro-organisms which have the additional function of mixing decaying organic and mineral matter. These microscopic plant and animal organisms require a moist and warm (over 10° C) habitat for their life and reproduction. Consequently there are certain moisture and temperature limits on the process of organic decay; these in turn are controlled by local climate above and within the surface organic layer. The decay and incorporation of organic matter is influenced by other factors as well, not least the composition of the vegetable litter itself. Even the balance of moisture and air which is a control on the decay process is modified also by topography and soil materials. This spatial variation of organic decay is discussed in Chapter 6, 'Soil as an Organic Medium'.

Vegetation and soil formation. The plant factor usually plays a varied and important part in soil formation, and plant matter is an integral constituent of soil, both the living plant and that in different stages of decay. Perhaps more than any other factor of soil formation, vegetation is closely associated with the rest, particularly with climate and soil fauna. It is therefore difficult to isolate the influence of vegetation, its actual effect being conditioned by its integration with other factors, but certain of its characteristics may be used as an indication of its potential role. These are the quantity and the quality of the plant cover and the annual rate of decay of the plant litter, and they must now be examined in more detail.

The quantity of plant cover per unit area of the soil surface is simply a measure of the plant production, or the per cent plant cover of the total soil surface combined with the size of the plants. In environments without an adequate supply of soil moisture or where the cold extremes of temperature are experienced, plants will be absent, or present in minimal density. In such arid or cold environments, those plants that can survive have structural modifications to withstand local environmental conditions. Some are low growing in form and others are found in a sporadic distribution over the soil surface. In such situations, vegetation barely enters the soil formation processes, and has only slight importance as a soil-forming factor. In all deserts, the plant factor is of little consequence in weathering and pedogenesis. Wherever the plant cover is incomplete—that is, the cover is less than 100 per cent—the role of plants in soil formation will be reduced. Assuming that other conditions are favourable, the lack of organic matter in the soil may be responsible for a reduction in weathering, plant nutrient supply, and soil-forming processes such as leaching. In fact, a reduction in these processes is usually associated with a general decrease in the potential of the whole environment to form soil. In arctic and alpine areas of discontinuous plant cover, both the season of plant growth and of plant decay are short, approximately co-incident in duration and less than two months in the year. Because both plant growth and decay require similar conditions of moisture and oxygen, and almost the same temperature range, they may be regarded as active in approximately the same period each year. It is true that the period of plant growth is restricted by the events of the plant life cycle, and hence the period of decay, being directly limited only by temperature and moisture, tends to last a little longer. The fact that the process of organic decay can keep pace with the supply of organic litter in the majority of sites is extremely beneficial for the condition of soil and for all living organisms. Failure in this function leads to the accumulation of organic litter on the soil surface, and eventually to the formation of peat.

In a given area, a discontinuous plant cover will not even make contact with, let alone affect, some of the soil, and its annual vegetable production will be small. Where or when the plant cover becomes complete, it is likely to increase its height with more favourable environmental conditions, and hence its total vegetable production. These developments are related partly to the length of the growing season, assuming that the moisture requirements of the whole plant community continue to be satisfied. In low latitude, tropical humid environments, there is no climatic limit on the growing season. Vegetable production takes place all the time, and fortunately the same applies to vegetable litter decay. The state of the organic matter in the soil is usually assessed by the ratio of carbon to nitrogen in the surface organic horizon. It is found that a relatively high proportion of carbon (commonly 50 times and sometimes even 100 times the nitrogen) is present in fresh organic litter, but in all sites where organic decay is encouraged within the normal limitations of microclimate, the ratio decreases rapidly to level out at a value of about 10. This is regarded as one measure of stability in the soil-forming system, and the same value applies universally wherever decay keeps pace with the supply of organic litter to the soil surface. The time taken to reach this stable ratio varies considerably with several environmental factors, and with otherwise comparable sites will most rapidly be reached in tropical humid environments. In these environments, the fastest rates of growth and decay, as well as attainment of carbon/nitrogen stability, are to be found. Organic decay may be prevented or inhibited by site wetness, either from a climatic or topographic source, and under these conditions, the trend toward carbon/nitrogen stability may be indefinitely postponed.

Also notable as part of the influence of vegetation on soil formation are features of the plant community such as form and structure which affect the route and timing of the supply of organic litter into the soil. With tree, shrub, and bush vegetation most of the litter supply is that of leaves from above the soil, while the leaf litter of grass plants is supplemented by an equal or greater annual supply of dead root material below the soil surface. The fact that woody plants are perennial while many grasses have an annual growth cycle further contributes to the difference in annual distribution of litter supply. The timing of the supply of organic litter may be either continuous, as it is with apparently evergreen vegetation, or seasonal and restricted to a limited period each year at the start of a cold or drought season. Where supply is continuous, there is almost no surface accumulation of organic litter if decay is also continuous, but temporary accumulation of litter and peat formation can be found in cold environments which have a short annual period of decay. An example or the former is tropical rain forest and of the latter, high latitude coniferous forest and heaths.

The quality of biochemical composition of the plant cover also qualifies the rate of organic decay and hence the state of organic matter in the soil. All vegetable litter contains a large proportion of carbonaceous matter, and woody material or leaves with extra cellulose thickening in their cell walls contain a specially high proportion. The period required for decay depends very largely on the amount of oxidation necessary to reduce the carbon to a value only ten times that of the nitrogen present. Larger amounts of the same vegetable litter provide an increased food supply for, and so help to multiply the population of, decay micro-organisms present. Thus the decay of additional vegetable litter of the same composition is assured within approximately the same time as for a lesser quantity, if all other variables remain constant. However, a change in the quality of the litter will alter the rate of decay even if the amount remains the same, and the time taken will depend on the quantity of carbon to be oxidised, assuming other conditions remained unchanged. In other words, with the same site and climatic conditions, litter with the highest carbon/ nitrogen ratios in the fresh state will survive longest as discrete organic matter, resisting natural decay and conversion into carbon dioxide, humus, and mineral constituents. Conversely, litter with low carbon/nitrogen ratios such as that from grasses is most quickly decayed by the same population of micro-organisms working on uniform quantities under uniform conditions. Thus, for example, decay of grasses and herbaceous plants is normally complete before the next growing season if conditions conducive to decay exist, but with the same conditions it may take several years to decompose vegetable litter from coniferous needle-leaf trees or heath plants and incorporate it into the soil (see Chapter 6).

The chemical composition of the original vegetable litter also influences the nature of organic solutions that, under well drained conditions, pass down through the soil from decaying organic matter on the surface. This solution is called the *leachate* and is the means of carrying certain soluble substances from upper to lower horizons of the soil in the soil-forming process of leaching. The chemistry of this process is discussed elsewhere in detail, but here it is relevant to mention the influence of different types of plant matter on the leaching process. Bloomfield (1953) has shown that certain organic extract solutions are more effective than others in carrying dissolved compounds. Each plant species has several organic acids present in its vegetable litter, and the dominant one will determine the mobilising power of the organic solution from that particular leaf litter. Maximum mobilisation of leachable substances is related to both the volume and composition of the organic leachate, and is not related to a specific pH value on the acidity scale. Thus, organic solutions of conifer needle-leaf litter have their greatest effect in dissolving iron compounds in extremely acid or low pH values, while solutions from some broadleaf litter from aspen, ash, etc are most successful in mobilising metallic ions in a narrow pH range at neutral to alkaline conditions. It is true that the latter are relatively less effective as leachates than solutions from needle-leaf litter.

Other biotic factors in soil formation. It is customary to distinguish between the influence of higher forms of plant life that make up vegetation and all other organisms when discussing the five soil-forming factors. The other organisms are all animals, with the exception of very primitive plants—the micro-flora—among the micro-organisms responsible for organic decay in soil. The micro-flora (bacteria, fungi, and algae) are simple plants, but have many functional similarities in common with the micro-fauna. The success of their task of decomposing vegetable litter depends on the provision of a suitably warm, moist, and well aerated habitat, as well as on the composition of the vegetable litter itself and degrees of acidity of the mineral and organic matter. This process of organic litter decay and the role of specific groups of micro-organisms is discussed in Chapter 6, 'Soil as an Organic Medium'. Each species has its own ecological tolerance of temperature, moisture, air, and acidity so that the values of these elements in the soil micro-environment partly control the population size of each species present. There is, in addition, a complex chain system of predator-prey relationships among micro- and macro-organisms which acts as another stabilising factor on population size.

The higher forms of animal life that inhabit the soil or have the power to change soil characteristics are part of this soil-forming factor. Moles and other burrowing mammals help to cultivate the soil, even if their impact is usually on a local and limited scale. Of much greater importance is man, whose role as a soil modifier, if not soil former, is widespread throughout the inhabited world,

in many areas causing the destruction or removal of soil previously under cultivation. Soils are observed, recorded, and classified on the basis of their present
characteristics, so man as a cultivator must be recognised as part of the soil
formation system. Examples of his work as an agent of soil reclamation as well
as soil destruction are given in Chapter 7, 'Soil as a Resource'. Man-modified
and man-made soils must be considered on the same criteria as natural soils for
all purposes of research and soil classification. In reality, they co-exist on the
landscape and all should be considered as products of the same soil formation
system. Man-modified soils are often highly variable in property values over
time and space due to the differential treatment they have received.

Relief and soil formation. Relief enters the soil formation system in
several ways, most of which are indirect and work through other soil-forming
factors. The involvement of other soil-forming factors makes it difficult to
isolate the influence of relief on soils; certainly, it is not possible to find one
type of soil on slopes and another on level ground. Relief as a soil-forming
factor can be sub-divided into surface morphology, aspect, and altitude. The
last two provide basic reference for a soil site, but are really passive in the
process of soil formation; it is the associated climate and vegetation that are
the active factors. Surface morphology can be regarded as more closely involved in soil formation, although an argument in support of a passive role
could be made.

What is significant about relief in the formation of soil is not a simple and
direct value (such as a measure of the angle of slope), but its relationships with
parent material and soil drainage. These can be affected both by angle of slope
and position of the soil site on it. Where it can be demonstrated that a relationship exists between soil profile type and the angle of slope, a *clinosequence* or
toposequence of soils is said to exist. But it does not necessarily follow that the
angle of slope must make some difference to soil formation. For example, it
does not where the parent material is porous and excessively well drained, in
which case the groundwater table is probably well below soil profile depth.
The average level of the groundwater table is then the critical factor in condi-
tioning the drainage of the soil body, and this varies according to the composition of the soil as well as with the surface morphology of the terrain. It is true
that the latter is generally the more important of the two and that the ground-

water table usually follows a more modified amplitude than the terrain surface. It can lie very deep in the ground on hills and mountains. If the soil parent material is uniform on a slope, it is possible to find a sequence of soil sites with progressively deteriorating drainage conditions downslope, with waterlogged soils at the foot of the slope. This has been called the *hydrologic sequence* (Fig

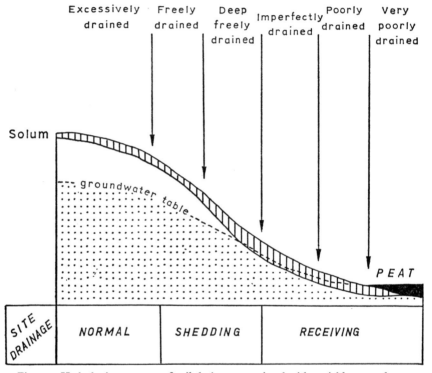

Fig 2:1 Hydrologic sequence of soil drainage associated with variable groundwater depth on a long slope, after Glentworth and Dion (1949). This is an ideal sequence only to be found developed on uniform soil parent material. The genetic type developed in each drainage category depends on the interaction of all soil-forming factors, and this slope sequence will be distinctive to a particular soil-forming environment

2:1); it is seldom found in practice as it is unusual to find such necessarily large areas of uniform parent material. There is, however, a good example along the south-east facing fault line scarp of the Scottish Highlands which is discussed in Chapter 8.

More commonly in the field, soil parent materials are highly variable over space and seldom uniform down any extended slope or across undulating terrain. Parent material variation and topographic variation can become inter-mixed in a complex relationship that makes it difficult to predict the type of soil being formed. If there is some recurrent regularity of parent material change with surface morphology, this can be represented diagrammatically as a chain or *catena* of change across a relief transect (Fig 2:2). Any other soil-

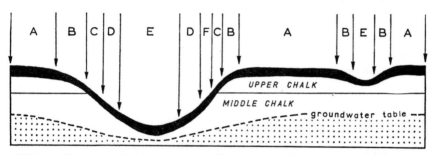

Fig 2:2   Soil catena showing repeating soil series units (A, B, C, D, etc) across dry valley topography in chalk with superficial deposits, Chiltern Hills, SE England—
after Avery (1958)

forming factor, such as vegetation or the state of soil drainage, can be re-presented by a soil catena if it also alters along a transect in a regular way with topography. A catena is a composite diagram which could comprise several clinosequences on individual slopes along it. It is not used much now in pedo-logical studies, but the fact that a different soil catena would have to be drawn for each soil-forming factor across any one area has some conceptual value in emphasising the multi-variable nature of soil formation.

Where soil parent material is highly variable on a slope, the particle size composition (called *texture*) can cause the water-holding capacity and possibly drainage of the soil to vary. Extremes of water-holding capacity, from that of porous coarse sand to that of impermeable clay, will interfere dramatically with the ideal hydrologic sequence of slope drainage. Unconsolidated materials may be moved downslope under gravity, either in a dry or in a lubricated condition. In this way, certain types of soil parent material sometimes become associated with a definite position on a slope, having themselves been affected by angle of slope and by gravity. The downslope movement may be by dry or wet flow, and may be current or relict from the past. On steep slopes with a dry surface, rolling action can move larger size particles if there is little plant cover to block the way down. Other types of mass movement include wet flow by soil creep and soil slipping, or fast movement mud and soil flows. Large scale movement of material is likely to happen over a lubricated subsoil whether this is a saturated or a thawing permafrost surface. The latter is known specifically as *solifluction* and in most areas of occurrence in high latitudes (north of 50° N at sea level) took place during the glacial phases of the Pleistocene period. Solifluction is still active now in high latitude and high altitude environments. Whether past or present, these various slope movement deposits are found at or near the foot of the slope, and appear roughly stratified in vertical sections.

However, soil formation is influenced directly by the physical and chemical character of the parent material and not by the landform type or origin of the deposit. The latter are of interest mainly as an indication of the former. Solifluction and slope creep deposits are usually loose, unconsolidated and well drained, as there is a tendency for larger size particles to dominate their composition. Their presence in foot slope zones does not by itself interfere with soil drainage. The reverse of this generalisation—and introduced here only to emphasise the contrast—is where soil itself is the causal agent in land form evolution. For example, in soil-forming environments such as in the humid tropics, highly compacted and cemented layers develop within the soil as part of its evolution (see Chapter 3, 'Soil as a Three-dimensional Medium'), and these layers are subsequently resistant to the normal processes of fluvial erosion. Cemented layers can survive as elevated surfaces, being dissected where there has been a weakness in the consolidation. In this and other ways, pedogenic features can influence the development of relief.

Parent materials and soil formation. The two main groups of processes at work in soil—weathering and pedogenesis—can be considered parallel and

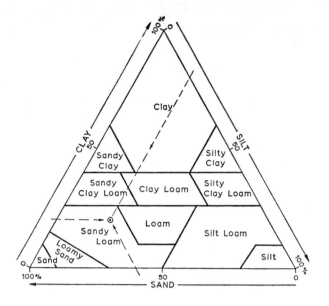

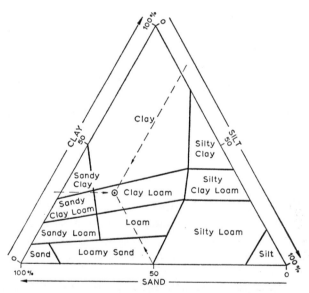

Fig 2:3 Two commonly used soil texture triangles which may be used to locate the texture class of a given soil sample, if its proportions of sand, silt, and clay are known (as indicated by arrows). The upper triangle is divided into texture classes to suit mechanical analysis by the American (USDA) system, and the lower one is for the international particle size range

interdependent. Certainly the rate of change in each is different, but they overlap and influence each other to a considerable extent and the original parent material is the starting point of both processes. The mineral composition influences the products of physical and chemical weathering—and these in turn influence pedogenesis. Although climate is the other major control on these processes, there are many examples within the British Isles, or any area of complex geology, where parent material differences account for much of the spatial variation in soil.

The mineral composition of the parent rock or transported deposit is a major control on the physical and chemical properties of the soil. Often soils develop on previously weathered material that has been transported by ice, water, wind, or under gravity. In these cases, transportation merely interrupts the processes of weathering and provides a deposit for soil profile development. Even where the parent material is rock in place, the weatherable minerals—or what has survived complete chemical weathering—are of continuing importance for soil profile development.

The principal primary or rock-forming minerals are:

1 Quartz—very resistant to weathering, chemically inert and so useless for plant nutrition, makes up sand fraction and is the most common mineral in sandy soils.

2 The ferro-magnesian minerals or calcium magnesium silicates—*hornblende, augite,* and *olivine*—contain iron, aluminium, calcium, magnesium, and trace elements, weather easily and are important as a supply of these elements as plant nutrients.

3 Felspars—sodium alumino- and calcium alumino-silicates—are almost as hard as quartz, decompose slowly to form clay minerals such as montmorillonite and kaolinite.

4 Micas—contain potassium, aluminium, magnesium, iron, hydrous silicates or phyllosilicates—weather quite easily, especially biotite mica, to form clay minerals such as illite, chlorite, and vermiculite.

5 Carbonates—calcite and dolomite—very soluble minerals. Weathering of rocks containing these carbonate minerals leaves only insoluble impurities as the soil.

In mid and high latitude environments, soil parent materials usually have a

Buried organic horizons, the former surface horizons of fossil soil profiles, emerging from mobile sand dunes at Dundrum, Co Down, Northern Ireland

reserve of these minerals, as well as minor accessory minerals, to be weathered in the future. Only in humid tropical areas is there a possibility that the soil might be composed of only secondary and tertiary products of chemical weathering. Also it should be recalled that some of the supply of chemical nutrients to plants from the soil comes through the decay of plant litter, eg, nutrients like nitrogen, phosphorus, sulphur, and some calcium, so soil fertility is not solely related to parent material composition.

The products of physical weathering are usually large on the particle size scale; that is, they are stone, gravel, or sand size and less commonly as small as silt size. Some of the silt particles and all the clay are produced by chemical weathering. This is the range of particle size:

		Old international scale	USDA American scale
Stones	100 mm (> 1 cm)	Coarse sand 2·00 mm–0·2 mm	2·00 mm–0·2 mm
Gravel	2–100 mm (< 1 cm)	Fine sand 0·2 mm–0·02 mm	0·2 mm–0·05 mm
Fine earth	2 mm and less	Silt 0·02 mm–0·002 mm	0·05 mm–0·002 mm
		Clay < 0·002 mm	< 0·002 mm

The size of silt was increased by the Americans to include most wind-blown particles within the silt range. These categories of particle size—sometimes called the soil separates—are mixed in any soil into what is called its *texture*. This is classified into a range of classes including sandy types (light textures) dominated by sand, loam or medium textures containing similar proportions of sand, silt and clay, and the heavy or clayey textures. They are usually represented on a triangular diagram (Fig 2:3). As a general rule, the clayey textures, having more than 30 per cent clay, tend to inhibit the passage of moisture through the soil. Because clayey soils tend to retain moisture, such soils often have perched water tables. At the other end of the texture scale, extremely porous sandy soils are very easily leached and cannot retain certain chemical compounds, eg, some artificial fertilisers, for any length of time.

The texture class of a soil is closely related to the mineral composition of its parent material, particularly to the respective proportions of quartz and clay-forming minerals present. The contribution of chemical weathering to the physical properties of soil is mainly in the creation of clay minerals from the weathering of felspars and micas. If the parent material is rich in these clay-

(*Above*) Kunkar (the Australian name for caliche) cemented by calcium carbonate at a site near Adelaide, South Australia; (*below*) Australian kunkar, exhumed and exposed as the ground surface, acts as a control on the development of landscape morphology in South Australia (see page 96)

D

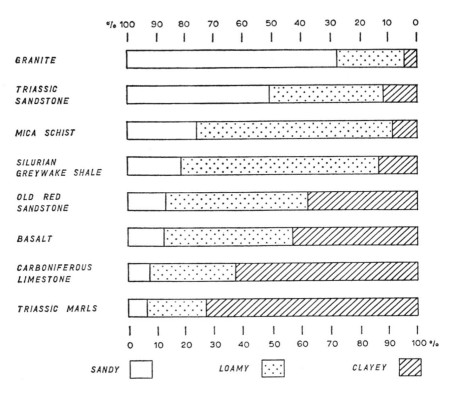

Fig 2:4 The percentage proportions of textural types found in soil samples from surface horizons in Northern Ireland. (Adapted from 'Soils', by S. McConaghy and J. S. V. McAllister, in *Land Use in Northern Ireland,* ed L. J. Symons, ULP, 1963.) Here soil samples are classified by the nature of their derivative rocks.

Sandy textures require > 50 per cent sand
Loamy textures require > 60 per cent sand > 20 per cent silt
and < 40 per cent clay
Clayey textures require > 30 per cent clay

forming minerals, then there will be a correspondingly high clay fraction in the soil texture. Some clay minerals expand on wetting, which is both chemically and physically important to a soil. It happens because clay minerals have a layered or lattice structure which expands and contracts according to how much moisture is held within it. If, however, quartz dominates the original material, little clay will be produced and sandy textures are the result. The influence of rock type on soil texture is shown in Fig 2:4.

The second major physical property of soil is *structure*, the natural scaffolding of the soil. There are four main types of soil structure and their geographical distribution is influenced by the texture, the presence of cementing agents and by pedogenesis. The four possibilities are platy, columnar, blocky, and spheroidal structures, as shown in Fig 2:5. Partly decayed organic matter in the form of humus, along with calcium and magnesium ions, act as bonding or cementing agents to make the most durable structural units. The soil particles first join together to form aggregates and these group together to form the structural units, called *peds*. Closely packed and well cemented structures such as the horizontal, platy type tend to impede and even halt the passage of moisture, while more openly packed crumb structures facilitate soil drainage. The latter is usually associated with humus-rich horizons, particularly cultivated surface horizons.

The physical and chemical soil properties so far discussed have been assumed to be the product of the weathering of mineral parent material. These properties can be altered later through pedogenesis. However, the most important characteristics of parent material for subsequent soil development are the mineral composition and the degree of weathering reached. The former affects physical properties and the supply of mineral nutrients available to plants, while the latter is an indication of the chemical resource left in the soil under natural conditions.

The origin of parent materials is not significant for soil development except as an indication of the soil properties that may be expected. Parent materials may be classified by their mode of formation as follows:

1   Weathered rock in place which produces residual soils.
2   Mineral material very similar in mineral composition to local rock, but moved under gravity by slope creep to form a stratified, unsorted col-

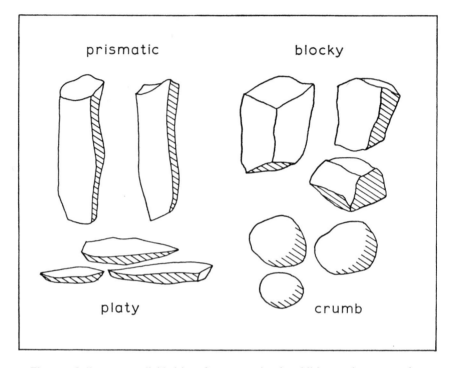

Fig 2:5   Soil structure divided into four categories, in addition to the structureless condition. Structural units (peds) are three-dimensional. Prismatic or columnar structure, vertical dimension longest, is associated with clay-rich soil. Blocky or cubic structure, almost equal dimensions, is associated with loamy soil. Platy structure, horizontal dimension longest, is associated with compacted or cemented horizons. Crumb structure (spheroidal shape) is found in organo-mineral soil usually with a loam texture

luvial deposit. In (a) and (b), soil properties will be influenced by the mineral composition of the local rock.

3 Material deposited by moving water—alluvial and marine deposits—stony, usually large particle size and sandy textures. Alluvial deposits are often waterlogged due to site conditions rather than physical composition.

4 Lacustrine deposits, water-laid in still water in which all the material in suspension eventually will be deposited. Lacustrine deposits are usually sorted into strata of different particle size, and often contain a large proportion of clay. With over 50 per cent clay, they will be almost impermeable to the passage of water.

5 Wind-blown material—aeolian deposits. Gravel and coarse sand grains are moved only a short distance even by wind of high velocity, but smaller silt and clay particles may be carried hundreds of miles. On deglaciation, exposed glacial till is a good source of wind-blown material. During the deglaciation phases of the Pleistocene glaciations, wind-blown silt was deposited on a spectacular scale in extensive, stoneless *loess*. Wind-blown material is usually 0·1 mm–0·01 mm in diameter, and hence relatively uniform in physical composition.

6 Glacial parent materials. (Under this heading, some parent materials similar to alluvial and lacustrine deposits may be included.) Water-deposited material in eskers and kames is of stone, gravel, and sand size as the water was usually moving at a considerable speed, and even under pressure in some cases. These are coarse-textured, bedded, and sorted deposits. Outwash alluvium is usually similar in texture, but may include some fine debris where the melt water has spread over a large area. These deposits usually develop porous, well-drained soils. The same may be said of glacial moraines which are usually composed of boulders, and other larger size and unsorted material. Because of the stoniness of the material and very irregular topography, glacial moraines are very difficult to cultivate for arable purposes and are quickly leached of applied fertilisers. Lacustrine glacial deposits are common, but usually limited to depression sites. They are used more as a source of material for brick making than for agriculture.

In glaciated areas, the most widespread relic of glaciation is till or boulder clay. This material, which is the parent material of so much soil in Europe and North America, derives its characteristics mainly from its parent or derivative rock. There are many exaggerated ideas about the action of sheet ice in the creation of glacial till. In fact, ice probably does no more than mix and push weathered material already *in situ*, and redistribute its thickness. In a glacial area, till depth is variable and can be interrupted by rock outcrops. Glacial till comprises mainly fine earth produced by pre-glacial weathering of the parent rock into which ice has mixed fragments of rock. The matrix of glacial till is derived from the rock on which it lies. Only in exceptional cases did sheet ice have the power to move the till matrix any distance from its derivative rock, and this distance is usually only two or three miles. However, erratic stones may be moved great distances and the orientation of these and other stones in glacial till may be used to establish the direction of ice movement.

Parent materials developed on and because of permanently frozen ground are found in areas that are, or have been, immediately extra-glacial or peri-glacial. The active layer above permafrost is so charged with moisture that it readily flows on thawing. It will move on any slope greater than 2° and stones in the material become aligned with their long axis in line with the direction of slope and parallel to the surface. In a section, the material appears to be stratified and the stones are usually very angular—having been produced mainly by frost shattering. In extra-glacial southern England and Ireland, there are considerable areas of such solifluction or 'head deposits' that have moved into their present position under gravity on lubricated slopes.

Time and soil formation. Soil evolution, stage, and maturity have long been cardinal concepts of pedological thought. Soil parent material was defined by Jenny (1961) as the state of the soil system at the beginning of pedogenesis, or in other words, at soil formation time zero. Soil-forming processes act on the parent material under a set of governing factors, and through time, tend towards a stage of maturity. This is difficult to define, and has provoked so much argument among pedologists that the concept of a rigidly defined maturity has been abandoned. Some soil-forming processes progress continuously towards a minimal steady state while others try to attain an early equilibrium with environmental conditions. Those processes which have an accelerating rate of change, such as the leaching of highly mobile salts, can reach a steady state only with the nearly complete depletion of the leached compound. On the other hand, a repetitive and perpetuating process such as organic decay finds equilibrium relatively early with the carbon/nitrogen ratio at about 10. The latter example is a case of loss of material being balanced by supply. In the former case, it is possible for the degree of leaching to be arrested when one or more of the soil-forming factors compensates for the others to impede the progress of the process. But any significant change in any of the environmental factors alters the character and organisation of the soil-forming system, and theoretically provides a new parent material, putting the soil formation back to time zero. A sudden and major change, such as clearance of vegetation or a change of parent material by volcanic eruption or landslide, is necessary for soil formation to be considered a return to time zero. This should be considered as exceptional. Gradual variation of any or all of the factors produces a continuous change in the soil formation system and hence a continuous change in parent material. Under natural conditions, the effective mixture of the soil-forming factors is always changing, and consequently what we see as contemporary soil merely represents a stage in a continuous development.

Soil is a product of several processes which are not synchronous in their respective rates of working. It can be argued that all the soil-forming processes must be judged to be in equilibrium before the same assessment can be applied to the whole soil body. Certainly there are many problems involved in identifying the equilibrium condition of a soil; if only a few soil properties are considered, only partial equilibrium may prevail. Pedologists naturally have become accustomed to measuring certain properties for which there exist well tried techniques of measurement. Moreover, uncertainty easily arises in comparisons among soils developed by different sets of environmental factors because the morphological expression of equilibrium may not be the same. Soils may be in equilibrium with their environment without having marked horizon features in their profile, and, vice versa, soils may have strongly de-

veloped profile features without being in equilibrium. The degree of horizonation is not necessarily a measure of stage of development. The morphological
appearance of a soil in equilibrium is almost as infinitely variable as soils
themselves, and the relatively slow rates of most soil-forming processes do
not encourage empirical investigation of this pedological problem. Research
studies concerned with time as a dimension of soil change are faced with two
main problems, (a) establishing soil formation time zero or the starting point
of the soil development, and (b) confirming the rates of the soil processes
involved. For absolute dating of soil age, it is necessary to know about both,
particularly as it is possible that slow process rates over a long period can
produce a soil with the same characteristics as are produced by fast process
rates over a short period. The establishment of a datum point requires the
presence within the soil of some material (containing carbon, potassium-
argon, etc) that has a measurable life cycle, or some man-made artifact or
evidence of some catastrophic event from within recorded time. These requirements usually result in examples of absolute dating of the initiation of soil
development being confined to recent or historical time. If much greater time
periods are involved, all that is possible is the relative dating of soils.

Pedological research has been able to investigate only comparatively short
periods of soil history, based mostly on archaeological evidence on a scale of
hundreds of years. However, this is not as limiting as it may appear because the
evolution of a soil to equilibrium usually falls within this period. Generally, the
rapidly changing part of the life of a soil—to the equilibrium or steady state
stage—takes hundreds or a few thousand years, while the weathering life of
parent material may last tens of thousands if not millions of years. Weathering
and pedogenesis, despite their interrelationships, are measured on different
time scales. It is important to make a distinction between them; pedogenesis
may revert to zero time in certain circumstances, but weathering continues the
same life cycle unless fresh parent material is introduced. A second distinction
is that the rates of change of these two processes can have a variable relationship. In tropical and sub-tropical humid environments, both processes take
place rapidly and it is possible for a new soil to come into equilibrium with its
environment within tens of years. But in high latitudes, conditions are much
less favourable for weathering and it is possible for the rate of pedogenesis to

be fast despite slow weathering. In the latter situation, sandy, porous parent material exposed to effective leaching solutions can develop soil profiles to equilibrium in a relatively short time, while weathering may progress very little. After the draining of a lake and marshy ground in central Sweden it was noticed that the first signs of a new soil profile forming (a podsol) were apparent at 100 years and it was projected that the equilibrium stage found in comparable surrounding sites would be reached within 1,000 years. A coarse sandy deposit in Sherwood Forest, near Nottingham, England, also showed signs of podsol features only 25–30 years after replanting with pine, having previously been a brown earth under an oak dominated mixed woodland. In this case equilibrium as a podsol might be attained in about 200 years, judging by progress under older conifer plantations in the district. Of course, in these examples the morphological evidence is easily seen.

It is impossible, however, to make generalisations about rates of profile development even within broad limits for the major environments of the earth's surface, as they depend so much on the local interaction of the soil-forming factors. Recently, soil development was investigated at a former Indian village in Canada (Cahiague, Ontario) which was known from recorded sources to have been abandoned for at least 300 years (Cruickshank and Heidenreich, 1969). Top soil that had fallen into grain storage pits, presumably about 300 years ago, showed almost no sign of pedogenic change towards the local soil profile type which was a strongly differentiated podsol. The site had similarities with the two cases previously mentioned, ie, porous sandy material and a mixed conifer–deciduous woodland cover. The explanation suggested in this case for the minimal leaching rate was that because the soil is frozen for about four months each year, there is only a small amount of excess precipitation for soil leaching in spring and autumn. Moving further into high latitude continental interiors and polar environments, the annual duration of, and hence the rate of, leaching becomes less as the season of moisture immobility becomes longer.

Sandy parent materials and, in particular, coastal sand dunes have been favourite sites for the measurement of soil process rates. Early work by Salisbury (1925) on the Southport dune system (Lancashire, England) revealed an exponential relationship between the removal of calcium carbonate from surface soil and time. The age of the sand dunes was assessed by an examination of old maps (1610 and 1736) and *dendrochronology* (time measurement based on identifiable tree growth), made possible by the early arrival of *Salix repens* in the intervening hollows. A very similar relationship was established by Burges and Drover (1953) from a study in New South Wales on parallel sand ridges that were dated by assuming a constant eustatic change in sea level, the initiation of which was determined absolutely by radiocarbon dating. In both cases, a period of between 200 and 300 years was required to remove virtually all of the calcium carbonate from the top 15 cm of the soil and reduce the pH value to 6·1. Removal of iron compounds became visible in the Australian soils in the 300 year old material, and a clearly defined podsol profile was found in 2,000 year old sand deposits. Even with otherwise constant soil-forming factors, the rate of pedogenesis varied with plant cover and it was thought that a podsol in equilibrium with its environment would require 2,000–4,000 years, according to vegetation type, in this Australian example.

The relative weathering age of parent materials can be estimated in several ways when based on the assumption that the original materials had the same or similar mineral composition and have been exposed to the same or similar weathering conditions during their respective lifetimes. As these conditions are rather strictly specified, they limit the range of parent materials that can be compared. One method (van Wambeke, 1962) is to assess the weathering age of parent material from the amount of physically weathered material of silt size as a proportion of the chemically weathered clay minerals. In other words, this is an attempt to use, as a measure of age, the degree of chemical weathering reflected in the amount of weathered clay compared with the mineral reserves, in the form of silt, remaining to be weathered. Relative weathering age among similar parent materials—and this method is applied usually to the weathering of rock of known composition—is based on their silt-to-clay ratios. In the case of granites, a ratio of less than 0·1 indicates a Tertiary age beginning for a weathering period of tens of millions of years, while one greater than 0·4 indicates a period since the recent Pleistocene age. With basalt, the range of values is from 0·1 to 1·03. The per cent proportion of unweathered minerals remaining in the fine sand fraction (usually between 10 and 60 per cent) may also be used as an indication of relative age. With glacial tills that may have experienced intermittent chemical weathering since their rock origin, a method of measuring their respective depths of removal of carbonates is used to estimate the time since till deposition. As other factors are involved in the carbonate removal, this method also requires the respective tills to be of similar and known composition and particularly that their original calcium carbonate content be known. It must be assumed that the difference in the depth of removal of carbonates is due only to the time difference for which constant leaching has been operative and that the rates of removal have been uniform among compared sites. In tropical or formerly tropical environments, where the longest period of undisturbed conditions have occurred, the relative age of parent materials may also be estimated by association with geomorphological surfaces formed during landscape evolution. This has been done in Australia where relative soil age can be correlated with a sequence of erosion surfaces, produced in what are known as 'K cycles' (Butler, 1959).

A distinction has already been made between weathering and pedogenesis with regard to absolute dating, and the same distinction should apply to relative dating. The techniques previously discussed for the relative dating of parent materials do not refer to and cannot be used for pedogenesis or the age of the soils themselves. Soil profile development is conditioned by many more factors than weathering and these factors are variable over time and space. Age comparisons among soil profiles are based on established theories of soil formation rather than on techniques of direct measurement. Russian pedologists (Viliams, 1939) and some western soil geographers (Carter and Pendleton, 1956) have interpreted the pedogenesis in all humid environments from cold to hot as belonging to a single pedogenic process, so that soil profile differences attributed to climate are simply a function of time. Attempts to broaden this theory to include pedogenesis of all sites and environments, as originally proposed by the Russians, have been dismissed long ago; but only some modification is necessary to accept the concept for freely draining sites of humid environments. This framework of one compound process (an aggregate of many complex chemical, physical and biological processes acting either concurrently or consecutively) does allow a comparison of the principal soil profile types by their stage of development. This does not necessarily mean that a particular soil profile will inevitably pass through all the well-defined stages of the compound soil process before it reaches equilibrium. The complete sequence can be passed through by one soil if the soil-forming factors change during the soil evolution at the site, or are conditioned from the outset to encourage pedogenesis to the ultimate stage. It is more common, as is evident from the infinite variety of slowly changing soil types in humid environments, to find soils reaching equilibrium with their local environment long before the end stage of the sequence and changing very slowly thereafter. Specific examples of the time sequence relationships among soil profiles are described later (Fig 3:4); here, it is important to repeat that time is not a soil-forming factor in the sense of climate or vegetation. The five soil-forming factors exist in time as well as space, and therefore time cannot function as an independent variable within the soil formation system. Time is passive, and should be regarded only as a dimension of soil development.

Soil energetics and the soil system. It will be apparent to the reader that the functioning and interaction of the five soil-forming factors can be compared with some kind of working organisation. Sometimes it is called a *system*, and it can be defined as a special type of system through which there is a flow of materials and of energy. The soil formation system is what is called an *open system*, as distinct from a *closed system*; both belong to the systems concept as outlined in the Theory of General Systems. This theory was advanced in 1955 by American physicists and engineers, but based on earlier work, to embrace all functioning organisations in any branch of science provided they could be defined as systems or assemblages of interacting and interrelated parts which perform work involving the transfer of energy and materials. Closed systems, which are most common in the physical sciences, are complete and self-contained. They have fixed components and a given energy budget at the start. There is no import of energy or materials in closed systems and they function by working through a predictable sequence of run-down until they reach a static end-stage, eg, a pendulum or a battery. In contrast, open systems are flexible, dynamic, and unpredictable. The components may change and there is a continuing flux of energy and materials through the open system. Energy is convertible into a variety of forms, but is indestructible. Interactions involving work may take place at irregular rates and the system is in a state of continuous change. There is no predictable end-stage in an open system, but a state of dynamic equilibrium can be attained at any time. All living organisations are open systems; examples are the soil formation system, the human body, an organic cell, a human or animal community, or an ecosystem. They all function on an input and output of energy and matter, taken from and returned to the environment around them. In all these open systems of nature, the original source of energy is from solar or light energy, only directly usable by plants but converted by them into chemical energy food supply for other organisms. The chemical energy stored in vegetable matter also makes its way into the soil formation system.

The role of the five soil-forming factors and time as components of the soil formation system may be examined according to their function in an open system. These five factors and time are rearranged into what have been called the three state factors of the soil system (Jenny, 1961). The first state factor is 'the initial state of the system, or its assemblage of properties at time zero when pedogenesis starts', and this combines parent material and relief. Secondly, there is the state factor that includes all the external elements outside the initial soil body (climate, vegetation, and fauna) which control the supply and loss of energy to and from the soil system. Jenny referred to them as the 'external potentials' of the energy flux through the system. The third and last of the state factors is time or the age of the system, which is a measure of the period for which there has been a flow of energy and matter through the system.

A soil system may gain energy and matter from outside its arbitrary boundaries by a number of inputs or influxes, some of which are:

1 Energy—from solar radiation and heat energy transfer from warmer to cooler areas, as well as converted light energy (solar radiation) as chemical energy in vegetable matter.

2 Matter (a) Gases such as water vapour, nitrogen, oxygen, and carbon dioxide which enter the soil system by diffusion or mass flow.

(b) Water in the form of rainfall, snowfall, or ice.

(c) Solids dissolved in water, such as nitrate and sulphate, and brought into the soil by rainfall, flood, run-off, or fertiliser application.

(d) Solids carried by wind from volcanic eruptions or effluents released into the atmosphere.

(e) Solids gained from the weathering of parent material and by mass movement of particles from adjacent soils.

(f) Immigration of mobile organisms—plants, animals, and man.

These and other inputs of energy and matter take part in reactions and processes in the soil system, involving a transformation and perhaps dispersion from their previous state. Eventually, they may be lost from the system, but energy, in particular, will never be destroyed. Following these pedogenic reactions, the flux of energy and matter is maintained by losses from the soil system in the following ways.

1 Energy—lost from the soil system by heat radiation and light reflection. Energy is also transformed and stored in the soil for long or short periods in the form of organic matter, as well as chemically weathered compounds.

2 Matter—(a) Gases by the loss of water vapour through evapotranspiration; oxygen, carbon dioxide, ammonia, and hydrogen sulphide gases respectively released through the photosynthesis, respiration, and decay of organic matter.

(b) Water lost by run-off, percolation, and seepage.

(c) Solids dissolved in water or weak acids and lost through soil leaching and surface run-off.

(d) Solids lost by mass movement, solifluction, fluvial and wind erosion.

(e) Emigration of organisms.

By such gains and losses, energy and matter flow through the soil system as an essential part of the working of all pedogenic processes. Physical and chemical weathering, considered part of the compound process of soil formation, also use energy to make change of state possible. The heat energy consumed is stored in the weathered products until they are lost from the soil. Organic litter also brings converted energy into the soil system. This stored chemical energy, originally derived by green plants from light energy, is released and lost from the soil system as heat radiation in the process of organic decay. Potential heat energy may be stored in soil organic matter for long cycles as peat or lignite. The multiple-stage process of soil leaching is responsible for the loss of matter, some of which contains converted and stored energy, from the upper part of the soil body. Part of the leached compounds are deposited in the lower zone of the soil, but some will be lost from the system through soil drainage and seepage. The water balance between the atmosphere and land or water surfaces both supplies and removes moisture in liquid and gas states to and from the soil system. The erosion and deposition of material by wind, water and gravity is another example of a dual character process affecting the soil. The colonisation of the mineral soil by plants and animals and their outward movement beyond the boundaries of the soil body is also a phenomenon of supply and withdrawal of matter which can affect the energy status of the soil systems.

Soil profiles, if regarded as representative of soil bodies or individuals, are a reflection of the energy flux through their respective soil systems. In this way, a soil profile, soil individual or a soil formation system can be recorded as a balance sheet of energy inputs and outputs, and even classified accordingly. Soils may be compared by the amount, state and distribution of energy in their systems. The gains and losses of energy and matter do not affect equally all horizons of the soil profile, and it is the differential in their effect that gives the profile its distinctive morphological character. Soils of the tundra and other high latitude environments, as well as those of the low latitude hot deserts, have a small total energy budget. They develop in soil-forming environments where external potentials of energy flux (climate, vegetation, and fauna) limit both the amount and annual period of energy input and output. Conditions suitable for weathering, plant growth, organic decay and leaching occupy only a brief period because of long seasonal drought or freeze, and hence the period of energy flow through the system is also brief. In more humid and warmer climatic environments, the external potentials allow a faster rate and a much longer annual period of energy flow so that the total energy budget of mid-latitude grasslands and woodlands is about three times greater than that of cold and hot desert soils. In the humid tropics, there is almost no climatic or vegetational limit at any time. The external potentials allow a continuous and a very fast rate of energy flow through soil systems, with the total energy budget being at least three times greater than that of mid-latitude humid soils and nine times that of desert soils. The distribution of energy within the soil system at any one time depends on local soil-forming conditions; for example, any that encourage the accumulation of organic matter will consequently tend to leave a high proportion of the energy input in storage. Just as these soil-forming conditions continuously change, so does the energy balance within any soil. It is another example of the dynamic character of the soil body.

Bibliography

ARKLEY, R. J. Climates of some great soil groups of the western United States, *Soil Science*, 103 (1967), 389–400.

AVERY, B. W. A sequence of beechwood soils on the Chiltern Hills, England, *Journal of Soil Science*, 9 (1958), 210–24.

BLOOMFIELD, C. A study of podsolization I, *Journal of Soil Science*, 4 (1953), 5–16.

BURGES, A. Time and size as factors in ecology, *Journal of Ecology*, 48 (1960), 273–85.

BURGES, A. and DROVER, D. P. The rate of podzol development in sands of the Woy Woy district, NSW, *Australian Journal of Botany*, 1 (1953), 83–94.

BUTLER, B. E. Periodic phenomena in landscapes as a basis for soil studies, *C.S.I.R.O. Soil Publ.*, No 14, 1959.

CARTER, G. F. and PENDLETON, R. L. The humid soil: process and time, *Geographical Review*, 46 (1956), 488–507.

CRUICKSHANK, J. G. and HEIDENREICH, C. E. Pedological investigations at the Huron Indian village of Cahiague, *Canadian Geographer*, XIII (1969), 34–46.

GLENTWORTH, R. and DION, H. G. The association or hydrologic sequence in certain soils of the podzolic zone of north-east Scotland, *Journal of Soil Science*, 1 (1949), 35–49.

JENNY, H. *Factors of soil formation*, McGraw-Hill, New York, 1941.

JENNY, H. Derivation of state factor equations of soils and ecosystems. *Proceedings of the Soil Science Society of America*, 25 (1961), 385–88.

NIKIFOROFF, C. C. Weathering and soil evolution, *Soil Science*, 67 (1949), 219–30.

(*Above*) Caliche ground surface in Mexico; (*below*) caliche—calcium carbonate cemented horizon—about one metre in thickness at a site in Mexico (see page 96)

OLLIER, C. D. *Weathering*, Geomorphology Text 2, Oliver and Boyd, Edinburgh, 1969.

SALISBURY, E. J. Note on the edaphic succession in some sand dunes with special reference to the time factor, *Journal of Ecology*, XIII (1925), 322–28.

VAN WAMBEKE, A. R. Criteria for classifying tropical soils by age, *Journal of Soil Science*, 13 (1962), 124–32.

VILIAMS, V. R. *Pedology*, Moscow, 1939.

VOLOBUEV, V. R. Some questions of the energetics of soil formation, *Russian Soil Science*, 7 (1958), 722–28.

(*Above*) The remains of a cemented plinthite horizon protecting pallid horizon clay below as the ferralitic tropical soil is destroyed by fluvial erosion; (*below*) fossil plinthite surviving over the pallid layer of a former ferralitic soil, and currently defining a wave-cut platform (see page 96)

E

CHAPTER THREE

Soil as a Three-dimensional Medium

Introduction

IT HAS LONG BEEN RECOGNISED THAT SOIL IS A 'CONTINUUM' IN TIME AND space. It is a three-dimensional mantle of weathered mineral and decaying organic matter that changes continuously, in most cases gradually and in some cases abruptly, over space. There are relatively few sharp changes in the soil mantle on the horizontal or areal dimension and these few are controlled by factors extraneous to the soil itself. Obviously the soil body will have clearly defined areal boundaries where these are created by shorelines, rivers, geological faults, rock outcrops or even, in some cases, a long established plant community. But otherwise, and this is far more common, considerable areas can be found without such clear boundaries, the three-dimensional soil body changing slowly, often irregularly, and variably in all horizontal directions away from an observed point. Because of the continuous nature of soil change, both spatially and with time at any one place, the soil is described as a continuum.

This continuum of change creates difficulties in the organisation of soil field study. It raises questions of the identity of soil units and how these should or could be classified. It demonstrates that soil-forming processes should be investigated and measured both chronologically and spatially, the latter involving consideration of all the complexity of a three-dimensional medium. The soil body has depth, but this vertical dimension is not easily defined. The upper boundary is obvious, but the lower one may be either the maximum plant rooting depth or the base of the pedogenically altered material. It is assumed that the deeper of these two boundaries is taken as the floor of the soil

74

mantle or *solum*, but the definition is vague and the boundary is difficult to see on field inspection. Whatever the physical challenge may be in digging frequent inspection holes, a lower limit to the soil mantle does exist and is there to be found. It is more difficult to find areal boundaries to soil units, and the soil investigator may be influenced in his search by whether he is seeking a unit that is mappable on the basis of visible features, or one that has some functional significance. Through most of the history of soil survey, mapped soil units have been large or very large in size, arbitrarily defined by soil surveyors on the basis of field characteristics. But during the last two decades, new pedological concepts have focused on the problem of identifying a basic soil unit. Suggestions have been derived from developments in the theory of general systems as well as from re-thinking the principles of taxonomy in applying them to soil.

The argument and discussion that has arisen over different ideas about soil units is due largely to this fact that soil is a continuum in four dimensions—when time is included as the fourth dimension—and is not organised in discrete units. The challenge for pedologists has been to justify their own definition of a soil entity or individual within that context. Disregarding the time dimension as not immediately relevant to this problem, pedologists have known that, spatially, soil entities must be three-dimensional, having length and breadth (or area) as well as depth. As long ago as 1953, Crowther considered that soils were multi-dimensional but until recently the two-dimensional face of a soil profile was the only basic unit of soil field study. Shortly after the formulation of the general systems theory, Hans Jenny (1958) proposed a three-dimensional landscape unit to embrace both soil and vegetation and at the same time function as an open system. He argued that precise spatial boundaries were unimportant and could be drawn arbitrarily to any size. Jenny had in mind very small areal dimensions of less than one square metre so that the spatial continuum of soil change could be accommodated by a mosaic of basic units. Indeed, he named them *tesseras* after the name for mosaic tiles on the walls of Byzantine churches. The soil was seen as a functional unit integrated with plant and animal life, or what could be regarded as a mini-ecosystem through which there was a continuous flow of energy and matter. Its vertical dimension stretched from the top of the vegetation down to the soil parent material. It had to be a three-dimensional unit to function as an open system, but the actual spatial boundaries were not regarded as vital to its functioning. The tessera was introduced as a basic unit recognising both the open system and three-dimensional characteristics of the soil body, and furthermore to demonstrate that there was no real or clear boundary between mineral soil and the organic matter overlying or within it.

While the tessera has not been adopted in common usage, the concept embodied in it reappeared in a slightly modified form as part of the new soil classification and terminology proposed by the United States Soil Survey staff in 1960. This time the basic three-dimensional unit referred only to the soil body and was called the *pedon* (from the Greek word for ground). It is the minimal, three-dimensional form that can be given to the two-dimensional soil profile, and in fact, had been the conceptual soil unit in the mind of every pedologist when examining a soil profile. For that reason, pedon and profile will be used interchangeably in this text. The three-dimensional unit of the pedon must extend from the soil surface into the parent material so that a full set of soil horizons is included, but its areal or spatial dimensions need be only large enough to allow the pedon to be observed and sampled. Possibly the areal dimensions could be as small as ten centimetres in diameter for a roughly circular shape, giving the pedon an elongated columnar or prismatic form. Thus the form and concept of the pedon is very similar to that of the earlier tessera, except that the latter also included associated plants and animals. Both are elongated cores through the living skin of the earth and both must have horizontal areas small enough to minimise horizontal variation within the unit. It is accepted that the horizontal area of the pedon is no greater than one square metre unless horizons are intermittent, in which case a larger horizontal area becomes necessary to include all horizons. Pedons are described as if they were soil profiles, horizons being designated, observed and measured, except that the three-dimension form of the horizons is also reported. Inter-tonguing of horizons is recognised as a possible attribute of pedons.

Pedons have such minimal horizontal area that often they fail to reflect important features of the larger soil body. They deliberately ignore features such as the configuration of the soil surface and any lateral change to soil horizons. To reflect all the characteristics of the three-dimensional soil body, a collection of pedons must be put together to comprise an acceptable 'soil individual'. This collection of pedons is known as the *polypedon*, Fig 3:1. It is composed of one or more similar, contiguous pedons, and has no upper size limit. It is the smallest soil unit that could be mapped, although the basic mapping unit, the *soil series*, is usually composed of more than one polypedon. Each polypedon may include some variety, within defined limits, among its constituent pedons. Contiguous polypedons, each with some impurity, can be amalgamated into a soil series mapping unit if they are similar enough to conform to the soil series specification. A soil series is a soil mapping unit composed of the same or similar pedons (or profiles) on a single soil parent material. Its boundaries are not usually clearly defined, but are more often merging over a transitional zone. This supports the idea of the soil continuum, but creates

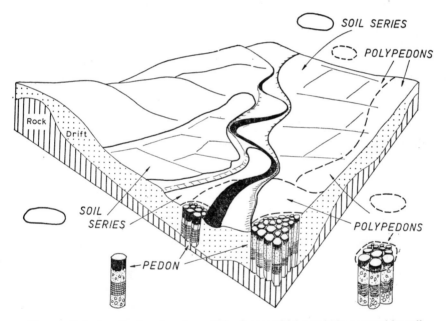

Fig 3:1   Pedons and polypedons in a soil landscape which would be mapped by soil series units

problems for the soil surveyor who must show boundaries by lines drawn on a map.

The term pedon is also used as a suffix to describe the three-dimensional form of certain soil horizons, in particular various types of surface horizon known as *epipedons* (or skin pedons). An epipedon is the surface part of the soil that is darkened by organic matter, or the upper eluvial horizons, or both. It is easy for the observer of soil to imagine the three-dimensional form of the whole soil mantle and even the surface soil horizon (indeed sometimes these two are taken to be the same thing), so it is appropriate to use polypedon and epipedon respectively for these soil units. It is often much less easy to imagine, quite apart from exploring and measuring, the three-dimensional form of other soil horizons unless they have been laterally exposed by the stripping of upper horizons. Even then it is necessary for the horizon to have some striking quality of colour, composition, or compaction for its form to be visible.

The soil volume and its constituents. The soil body has volume. Its three-dimensional form provides the overall framework in which soil processes operate. Inside its framework, each soil individual (the polypedon) has its own distinctive character which is the product of pedogenesis and which in turn influences pedogenesis. The polypedon is regarded as a collection of constituent pedons each with a set of soil horizons, but in a slightly different sense each soil horizon can be represented by a characteristic mixture of organic and mineral matter, air, and water. This view of soil as a habitat for higher plants is called the *edaphic approach*, an approach mainly concerned with the study of soil as a medium for plant production. But soil composition is so closely related to pedogenic features, and is associated with soil horizons, pedons, and profiles, that it may be considered part of soil geography.

Soil is composed of dead and living organisms, solid mineral matter, air, and water. The organic component is usually present in relatively small proportions in per cent weight or volume, even in soils classed as organic soils. Soils can be in this category with only 20 per cent organic matter by weight, because this corresponds to a much greater volume proportion of organic matter which increases its capacity to hold water. Even small proportions of organic matter can be both influential in pedogenesis and valuable to the soil environment, as is fully discussed in Chapter 6, 'Soil as an Organic Medium'. In a freely draining and well aerated soil, such as is desirable in agricultural production, the organic and solid mineral matter comprise about half the total volume of soil in the solum horizons. In this part of the soil, decaying organic matter and mineral matter, both much affected by processes of alteration (organic decay and mineral weathering), are intimately mixed in the structural units of the soil. Because of the nature of this combination, the respective proportions of organic and mineral matter in one horizon are not liable to change rapidly, and neither will their combined fraction. Various types of horizon are characterised by particular proportions of organic and mineral matter; the rest of the soil volume—the pore space—comprises air and moisture. The proportions of air and moisture are dynamic, complementing each other and individually altering in response to extraneous factors. Such temporary fluctuations in soil air or water do not necessarily produce any pedological change.

Pore space. Pore space is a soil property of considerable pedological and edaphic significance. It is a more permanent soil horizon property than the soil air or moisture which fluctuate, sometimes quite rapidly, within the pore space. The pore space volume is divided by size between the *capillary pores*, microscopic passages among the aggregates of soil particles, and *non-capillary pores* around the larger structural units or peds. A soil with a high proportion of its volume as stones, gravel, and sand has a correspondingly high proportion of its pore space as macro, non-capillary pores, in this case around large soil particles and stones. Soils with clayey textures, dominated by microscopic clay particles, have much of their total pore space as capillary pores. Clayey soils also tend to develop large columnar peds which on shrinking produce non-capillary pores. These two types of pore function differently; capillary pores retain moisture (capillary moisture) by surface tension forces after the free drainage of soil water, while the non-capillary pores, normally air filled, only contain water intermittently during drainage or for longer periods when the water table rises. Well-managed cultivation, through ploughing, manuring, and drainage improvement, increases the total pore space and particularly the proportion of air in it. Good soil aeration is an important condition for optimal plant growth, providing as it does space and oxygen for the growth and respiration of plant root systems and associated soil organisms.

The pedological and therefore the environmental variation of soil pore space was investigated by J. C. C. Romans (1959) for Scottish soils. His measurements revealed that the greatest contrast between adjacent horizons was to be found in podsols. In the freely draining upper horizons of friable consistence, the pore space was 50–60 per cent of the total volume, while in a lower compacted horizon it fell to around 22–32 per cent depending on the composition of the parent material. The lowest value widely recorded in this study was 23 per cent; the 22–24 per cent range was commonly found in compacted horizons in granitic soils, only slightly higher values being measured in basic parent material with softer cementation. The physical conditions of these cemented horizons mean that the pore space, however small the percentage volume may be, remains dry and only air filled. Their formation, as part of the pedogenesis of a podsol in this case, creates a horizon impenetrable for soil moisture and plant roots, consequently altering the pedogenesis and increasing the moisture in the pore space of horizons above. The rooting depth for plants is limited by this kind of horizon, and trees in particular, being forced to have only shallow roots, become liable to uprooting by wind-blow. Compacted horizons are usually found at least fifty centimetres from the soil surface, but can be nearer in cases where surface horizons have been removed by erosion or surface creep.

Even poorly drained soils with a high percentage of clay have a higher proportion of pore space than these compacted horizons in podsols. Their pore space values fall in the range 30–45 per cent, although the actual air space remaining under poor drainage conditions would probably be less than in the compacted horizons. Relatively high values (around 40 per cent pore space) are found in poorly drained clay soil with a strongly developed prismatic structure. Where this structural development is absent in clay parent material or in upper horizons of peaty clay, the percentage pore space is about 30. In freely draining soils with a loam or sandy loam texture, the pore space will comprise about 50 per cent of the total volume, and high values up to 65 per cent have been recorded. In soil profiles with relatively uniform texture, structure, and organic matter in all horizons of the solum, there will be little variation in the percentage volume pore space among the horizons. The greatest range of values is to be found in strongly horizonated profiles—those with clearly visible horizon characteristics—such as podsols. The contents of the pore space also have a pedological association.

Most of the soil air should be present in the large non-capillary pores. The gaseous composition of soil air depends on the extent to which it has been affected by biological processes in the soil and the ease with which it is exchanged with atmospheric air. Plant roots and micro-organisms absorb oxygen from the soil air and release carbon dioxide into it during respiration. Therefore, in time, any sealed-off soil air becomes depleted of oxygen and enriched with carbon dioxide. Normally the carbon dioxide content of soil air in which there are living organisms is at least seven or eight times greater (CO_2 = 0·25 per cent) than that of the atmosphere (0·03 per cent). The proportion of oxygen is relatively less affected because of the much greater actual amounts present, and usually the variation is between 21 and 20 per cent. Nitrogen varies only a little around 79 per cent, being increased fractionally more in the surface soil horizon if fertiliser treatment has taken place. Differences between the composition of soil air and atmospheric air become greater with depth, or distance away from contact with the atmosphere, provided organisms remain present. Because the differences are so closely associated with biological activity they are least in winter.

Soil air is displaced from the non-capillary pores by water draining through the soil, called *gravitational water*. After all the soil moisture that can do so has drained away, the soil moisture status is at *field capacity* and the remaining moisture which is held by surface tension forces as a complete and continuous film around the soil particles in the small, capillary pores is called *capillary moisture*. This is the moisture used by plants, the soil solution diffusing through the cell walls of the rootlets by osmotic pressure. This is a force of attraction towards the denser solution within the root cells which ceases when it is counterbalanced by the forces holding the cell walls together. If freely draining soils are compared, volume with volume, a clay-rich soil with far more surface area in the capillary pores will hold more capillary moisture than a sandy soil at the same surface tension pressure. When the two soils of equal volume contain the same quantity of capillary moisture, the moisture in the clay soil has to be stretched further and consequently is held with greater surface tension pressure than that in the sandy soil. Water may also be present in soil as *hygroscopic moisture* which is held with even greater surface tension forces than capillary water. This moisture is not available to plants: it remains in soil as only a minute fraction of its total volume even after a soil sample has been oven dried to 105° C. Ice and water vapour have to be included as forms of soil moisture, but they play a negative type of role in pedogenesis. This is not to deny the influence of ice, in the form of permafrost, on soil formation processes.

Pedogenesis in a three-dimensional medium. Soil-forming processes take place in three dimensions and it is possible for soil solutions to move in any direction depending on the characteristics of the site and the soil body. So slow is the rate of pedogenic change that it is difficult to foresee researchers being able to quantify it, quite apart from specifically trying to evaluate contributions received from different directions. Considering the examples of those horizons which gain their distinctive character from an enrichment of calcium salts, humus or compounds of iron or aluminium, it is impossible, at the present stage of pedological research, to specify what proportion is derived from local weathering within the horizon and what proportion has been translocated from above, from below or laterally into the horizon. There will be obvious indications from the state of drainage and normal height of the water table as to whether the dominant direction of movement has been upward or downward, but this goes only part of the way to answering the problem of measuring the various components of multi-directional soil solution movement within the soil body. It is generally assumed that the dominant direction of solution movement is downward in humid and sub-humid environments, and upward in arid environments, in both cases under conditions of free drainage. But in any area, the climatic influence varies seasonally and even over shorter periods. The immobility of soil solutions, as in frozen and sometimes in waterlogged soils, and the lateral movement of solutions are not controlled by climate, but by conditions within the soil body.

The lateral movement of soil solutions is only partially affected by the angle of slope of the soil surface, although it does play a part in pedogenesis at sloping sites. Surface run-off, as a proportion of total precipitation, is increased with increase in slope angle of the soil surface so the soil body will probably receive less moisture from above than at otherwise comparable sites on level ground in the same area. However, the most important factor controlling the movement of soil solutions on sloping sites is the volume of freely draining soil between the soil surface and the permanent groundwater table. Where this volume is relatively small, or the water table is near the soil surface, most of the solution entering the soil is forced to move laterally downslope over the surface of the water table. At sites where the water table lies particularly deep, the volume of the soil body may have the capacity to allow most of the moisture it receives to pass vertically downward to the water table, however steep the slope at the surface.

Of considerable influence on the lateral movement of soil solutions, at any site, is the presence of a perched water table held above and detached from the main groundwater table by any horizon or stratum impervious to the passage of water. Mainly because it is likely to be near the soil surface, it will confine soil water movement within a thin surface veneer of the total soil body. These perched water tables may have a geological or geomorphological origin in the sense that they can be due to impervious rock strata or a deposit of clay (Fig

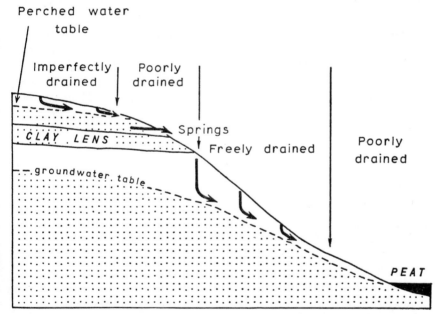

Fig 3:2   Soil drainage conditions associated with perched water tables

3:2). A lens of clay becomes impervious to the passage of more water once the macro-pores among the structural units have become filled. Clay pans can occur even at elevated sites such as drumlin summits and former lake-floor sites of a dead-ice landscape. Any cemented or compacted horizon, developed pedogenically, can function in the same way and support a perched water table with accumulating soil water. This phenomenon is, of course, encouraged by a humid climate and is rarely encountered in an arid one. The surface of a perched water table may coincide with the surface of a waterlogged clay-rich layer or horizon, but will have a separate level of accumulated soil water above cemented or compacted horizons which may be quite dry inside.

Soil profiles or pedons may cross and include perched water tables, and by definition must do so where the phenomenon is the by-product of pedogenesis. Cemented or compacted horizons occur in the middle or lower zone of the soil profile. Usually drainage is free prior to the formation of a cemented or compacted horizon, but subsequently the state of drainage and morphology of overlying horizons may change. Water accumulation over the impervious horizon creates surface gleying, shown by the mottled appearance of the mixture of oxidised and reduced compounds, and consequently changes the morphology of formerly freely drained upper horizons. The soil may be freely draining below the surface gleying. The cemented or compacted horizon resists the movement and erosive action of water so that in time it may emerge as an exposed capping or near-surface horizon after the removal of surface horizons by erosion. Pedogenesis responsible for the development of these resistant horizons is discussed later; at this point it is necessary to outline some general aspects of pedogenesis in a three-dimensional medium as background for more detailed discussion to follow.

Soil-forming processes: humification. A number of processes and stages in pedogenesis can be indentified, and some of the stages associated with distinctive profile types are discussed in the next chapter. Some processes that appear in the early stages of pedogenesis may continue during the whole life of the soil, and are equally important at all stages. *Humification* is a good example of one of these; it is the process of decay of organic matter. The life of a soil, as a medium for plant growth, begins only a fraction of pedological time before humification starts. As soon as the first plants die and accumulate on the soil surface as organic litter, the process of humification begins; subsequently it may have a considerable influence on other related soil processes. During humification, plant and animal residues on the soil surface are attacked by micro-organisms in a series of digestions and chemical reactions to produce humus, mineral substances, and the release of carbon dioxide gas. Decay is controlled mainly by temperature conditions and oxygen supply: a warm and well aerated micro-environment is conducive to the process, and encourages the change of most of the organic litter, leaving only humus, a soft dark-brown amorphous substance as a residue. Where local conditions do not promote organic decay as fast as the organic matter is accumulating, the raw organic matter produces its own organic solutions, probably mainly fulvic acid. In this latter situation, litter accumulates on the soil surface faster than the organic residues are being changed in humification. The surface organic horizon becomes thick, is quite separate from the mineral soil below and is raw, fresh, and relatively undecomposed. It is called *mor humus* in contrast to *mull humus*, the highly decomposed, and mineral-mixed type of surface organic horizon. These surface coverings of humus obviously have a three-dimensional form, and may merge into each other or into transitional types along all edges of an areal unit. Surface humus is discussed in detail in 'Soil as an Organic Medium'.

To consider the influence of only two types of surface humus is an over-simplification, if not a misrepresentation, of reality. Detailed explanation of the types and states of organic matter in the soil is given later, so here consideration is limited to the influence of mor humus and mull humus on pedogenesis in freely draining soils. Sites with organic residues and humus in quantity are found usually in humid or sub-humid environments which climatically encourage a downward movement of soil solutions, at least seasonally. Where the organic matter is fresh, weak organo-mineral solution combines with clay particles to keep them in a stable and flocculated state. Where the organic solution has a slightly more effective combination with the clay, and given sufficient moisture passing through the soil, clay particles will enter the soil solution and be physically removed downward through the soil body. This is called *eluviation*, and describes the physical movement of clay from upper to lower horizons in freely draining soils of basic to slightly acid reaction. Some physical change in the fabric and chemical composition at a lower level in the soil will initiate the deposition of the clay, which then becomes self-perpetuating and may even form a clay pan eventually. Under more acid organic litter, organic solution attacks the mineral silicates more effectively and combines with their iron and aluminium to form water-soluble compounds (chelation— see Chapter 6). These are kept in solution by organic fulvic acid, and carried downward or laterally through the soil body. A variety of explanations have been given for the mechanisms and reactions involved in bringing these weathered silicate minerals into solution in the first instance, and for their subsequent precipitation in a lower horizon of the soil profile. Technical difficulties involved in simulating field processes in laboratory experiments have not helped to solve the problem, which is perhaps the central one of all pedogenesis. This movement of iron and aluminium compounds, as well as that of other salts and substances, is a common characteristic of freely draining soils in all humid environments regardless of temperature regime. *Translocation* is the comprehensive term for all kinds of movement or redistribution of soil materials by pedogenic processes. It includes both the physical movement of clay particles in *eluviation* and the compound process of *leaching*.

Soil-forming processes: translocation. What is relatively well established is that the translocation or movement of substances in pedogenesis takes place in solutions of various types, and that the substances most easily dissolved will be the first to be moved. The direction of movement within the soil body will depend on local conditions, as previously discussed, but may be expected to be dominantly downward in humid environments. The most soluble or mobile compounds in soil are chloride, sulphate, and carbonate salts of calcium, sodium, potassium, and magnesium. Provided these are present in the soil, they will be dissolved by almost any moisture available and thereafter may be moved in any direction. Where the soil is in an arid or semi-arid environment, movement of soil solution is likely to be upward towards the drying soil surface by capillary attraction, and the accumulation of salts in a horizon near the soil surface is common. This movement is restricted as translocation takes place upward over only a short distance. In humid and sub-humid soils, these highly soluble salts are commonly removed or leached out of the surface horizons, being deposited low in the profile or carried right out in the soil drainage water. Because calcium carbonate salts comprise a large proportion of the total removal, the process is called *decalcification*. An investigation of the movement of soluble salts along a slope in Saskatchewan, Canada, has shown that they may move upward and downward, as well as laterally, through the soil body. Field survey indicated downward movement through the soil at upper or top slope sites, and lateral and upward movement at lower slope sites (see Fig 3:3). As these salts are so easily dissolved they are commonly found in any soil solution and are carried to wherever that is moving. The formation of cemented horizons by the concentration of calcium salts is called *calcification*.

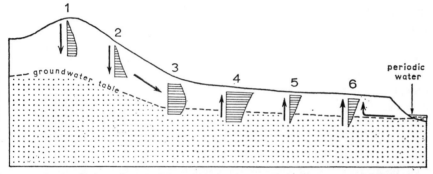

Fig 3:3 Direction of soil solution movement carrying the most mobile salts (sulphates and chlorides of calcium, magnesium, potassium, and sodium) at different positions on a slope, at a site in SE Saskatchewan—after Ballantyne (1963). The distribution of salts through the soil profile is indicated by the diagrams at each site

It is a by-product of the easy mobilisation of calcium salts, and under suitable conditions, can happen relatively early in the life of a soil. Mobilisation of soluble salts starts early in pedogenesis, given favourable conditions, and will continue as long as weathering provides chemical ions to enter soil solutions.

   In freely draining, humid environment soils, *humification* and *decalcification* are the first two stages of pedogenesis. Decalcification is the first stage of leaching. Sequentially, the next stage of leaching is *acidification* which is the result of increasing hydrogen ion concentration and involves the replacement of what are called the *exchangeable ions* by hydrogen ions from the weak organic acids of the soil solution. This exchange takes place on the surface of the microscopic particles of the soil—silicate clays and humus of < 0·002 millimetres or 2 microns in diameter—which form what is known as the *clay-humus complex* or *colloid*. This is the chemically active part of any soil, behaving as a colloid because it changes its state according to surrounding chemical conditions. In this way, it satisfies the requirements for a chemical colloid. It is stable and gel-like while its surface is saturated with exchangeable base ions (or basic cations) but becomes unstable and sol-like when these are replaced by hydrogen ions. This hydrogen replacement of base ions (calcium, magnesium, sodium, and potassium), held electrolytically on the surface of the clay-humus colloid, progressively makes it more acid and less stable as hydrogen ion saturation approaches. Ultimately the silicate clay colloid will dissociate into its constituent silica, iron, and aluminium compounds for translocation down through the soil profile. Soils rich in a supply of weathered calcium and magnesium ions may not reach this stage for a long time, remaining basic in all horizons. In an advanced stage of replacement of base ions by hydrogen, encouraged by decalcification in the soil outside the clay-humus colloid, the soil reaction becomes acid. The parent material reserves of base-rich minerals and the rate of replacement are the critical factors in controlling the time at which this stage is reached. Each soil horizon has its own distinctive size of clay-humus colloid surface, known as its *base or cation exchange capacity*, but although the size is highly variable, it is not necessarily critical in affecting the balance between supply and removal of exchangeable base ions. Those with a large clay-humus colloid are usually soils developing from parent materials most able to keep it stocked, while quartz-rich, sandy soils with small colloids are least able to keep pace with base ion replacement. It is these soils that reach acidification early.

The time-sequential relationship of these soil-forming processes is demonstrated in Fig 3:4. At the stage of humification only, there are a few embryonic soil profiles. With humification and decalcification only, freely draining soil profiles such as A (B) C brown earths are developed, and progress to acid brown earths as acidification occurs. When these processes are followed by losses of silica, iron, and aluminium from the silicate clays of the upper horizons and the translocation of their components into lower horizons by organic

(*Above*) Peaty podsol in which translocated humus is staining the Ae horizon above the spade handle. The spade lies against the orange-coloured Bf horizon; (*below*) iron pan podsol. The trowel lies across a thick (1 cm) iron pan which marks the junction between strongly developed Ae and Bf horizons (see page 97)

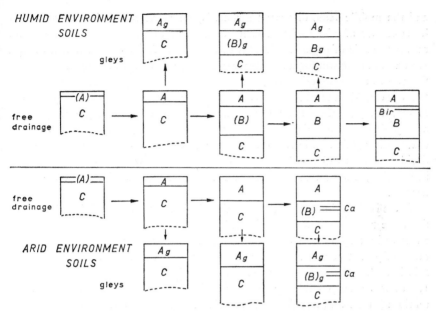

Fig 3:4   Soil profile relationships on a time or development sequence (see also page 105)

solutions, *desilification* takes place and *podsolisation* completes the compound process known as *leaching*. Desilification involves the loss of silica from the silicate clays by chemical weathering and removal by pedogenesis; it occurs in all humid environments, but in the tropics sooner than in others. Weathering in a humid-hot environment soil can modify the type of clay mineral present so that ultimately (in humid tropical soils for example) much of the silica is lost from the silicate clays, leaving them as 1:1 silica:alumina clays, eg, kaolinite. Under low temperatures, with discontinuous weathering and leaching, 2:1 silica:alumina clays like montmorillonite tend to survive for a long time, but in late stages of pedogenesis they may be subjected to desilification as well.

Podsolisation involves the translocation downward or laterally of iron and aluminium compounds from silicate clays, and their concentration in a specific lower horizon (B_2, B_f, or spodic horizon). The precipitation of these compounds

(*Above*) A humus-iron podsol with an over-burden of blown sand and thin organic bands marking former vegetation surfaces, on the sandy heathland of West Jutland, Denmark; (*below*) an acid soil, a podsol with thick surface peat, overlying alkaline chalk near Ballycastle, Co Antrim, Northern Ireland. This apparent anomaly is possible only because the podsol is developed completely within an acid schistose drift, and the chalk is the D horizon in this case

F

and the mobile salts, discussed earlier, is otherwise called *illuviation*; and B horizons are *illuvial horizons*. Consideration of this process of podsolisation recalls the role of organic solutions in freely draining soils mentioned earlier. Iron and aluminium form metal–organic complexes with the organic solutions from soil surface organic litter, but the actual acidity or pH value at which this takes place, and the pH range over which the metals stay in solution, appear to vary among different types of organic solution. Bloomfield (1954, 1955), in a very well known series of experiments investigating podsolisation, showed that even organic solutions at quite high pH values from the litter of broad-leaf deciduous trees and grassland could form complexes with iron and aluminium in solution, but that the pH range over which this could be sustained was narrow.

There is little doubt that the organic solution (probably mainly fulvic acid) from the base-deficient litter of needle-leaf conifers and heath plants is most effective in keeping iron and aluminium in solution over a wide, though acid, range of pH. Recent studies have shown that iron and aluminium remained in solution when the ratio of the combined metallic ion to organic acid was about 1, and was even possible up to a ratio of 3:1. Precipitation of iron and aluminium (in the sesquioxide form of ferric and aluminium oxide) was inevitable by the stage of 6:1 metal:acid ratio, and the laboratory investigation showed that the point of the precipitation within the profile was controlled by the reaching of the critical ratio of metal to organic acid. Once precipitation starts, it is likely to be self-perpetuating at that point in the profile due to the high and increasing metallic concentration, the greatest concentrations being found in the upper part of the precipitation or B horizon. Examination of the metal to organic acid ratio within the spodic or Bf horizon of podsols in another study in Canada (McKeague, 1969) confirmed that it was over 3:1 and could be as high as 9:1. This hypothesis for the precipitation of iron and aluminium is new, but attractive because it does not depend on conditions in the soil, is applicable in freely draining soils of all humid environments, and helps to explain the variable and erratic junction between the metal-depleted and enriched horizons. Earlier explanations for the precipitation of iron and aluminium oxides required a physical or chemical change in the soil composition to initiate the precipitation or illuviation. It is interesting to notice that the contrast between the chemical status of these two horizons is greatest in the contact area at their junction. Once the difference is established between the A and B horizons, it becomes progressively greater as podsolisation advances.

Cemented and compacted horizons. All soil horizons have a three-dimensional form, but those that have a clearly visible colour and texture such as the leached horizon of a podsol, or those that make their presence felt in a physically obvious way, are perhaps the most convincing examples. Those horizons which resist the spade have been cemented by one of several possible substances into a hard, concrete-like layer which prevents penetration of plant roots and reduces, if not prevents, infiltration of moisture. Such hard, compacted—sometimes described as indurated—horizons represent an extreme, but not unusual, product of pedogenesis in a variety of soil-forming environments. Cementing together of soil particles in these horizons creates a physical blockage to the downward drainage within the profile so that secondary pedogenesis in the form of gleying is subsequently promoted above and after the development of the cemented horizon. The cementing is also chemically irreversible, and being also resistant to erosion, allows the horizon to survive as a relict long after superficial horizons have been removed or the soil-forming environment has altered. In some cases, this process of *pedocementation* happened during the Quaternary period when precipitation was much more than at present. For example, in parts of Australia, South Africa, western United States, and the Mediterranean lands so affected by Quaternary pedocementation, indurated horizons have influenced subsequent landscape evolution and can now be found as surface capping horizons. They are so strongly consolidated that they appear and behave like a stratum of sedimentary rock. These rock-like qualities may be an advantage for building purposes in a few cases, but more commonly mark the beginning of the end of the soil as a medium for plant growth and agricultural production. In only some cases can machinery be used to fracture and redistribute the materials of a cemented horizon.

The agents responsible for pedocementation are silica, calcium carbonate, clay, and the sesquioxides of iron and aluminium. They act as cementing agents in a number of ways and over a range of environmental conditions. Hard, cemented horizons are known as pans and when cemented by silica they are *duripans*, by calcium carbonate they are *petrocalcic horizons* or *caliche*, by clay they are *clay pans*, mainly by ferric oxide they are *laterite* or *plinthite*, but iron along with organic matter forms *ortstein*. Thin crusts of mainly ferric oxide in podsols are called *iron pans*, and commonly found at depth in the same profile are *fragipans*. These are dense, indurated horizons with a platy structure that occur between the B horizons and parent material because of some kind of pressure and compaction during pedogenesis. The term *hardpan* is loosely used to describe all types of cemented horizon, whatever the cementing agent or position in the profile; its long and indiscriminate use illustrates the need for stricter definition of different types of cemented horizon, now partly answered by the United States Soil Survey's new terminology.

Horizons cemented by silica have been described as hardpans and silcrete, as well as duripans. They seem to develop from a variety of parent materials and weathering conditions wherever local climate is wet enough to carry weathered silica in solution, but not so wet that it encourages soil leaching. Silica in solution can be moved long or short distances, laterally as well as vertically, before it is deposited as a cement between soil aggregates. Duripans formed in Western Australia (see Fig 3:5) are said to have been cemented by silica that has moved great distances in solution, but in other cases the source of the weathered silica may be within the same or adjacent soil profile. It has been proved that a relatively small amount of silica (eg, 10 per cent of mineral weight) can cement a horizon into an extremely hard state that will resist dispersion in water or a sodium salt solution. This strength and stability of the silica cement is a notable characteristic of a duripan which explains the fact that its bulk density or volume weight is often similar to that of other noncemented horizons in the profile. In contrast, a high bulk density is a common characteristic of other types of cemented horizons.

Calcium carbonate accumulation and cementation is associated mainly with soils of arid and semi-arid environments, provided that the parent material is rich in reserves of calcium carbonate. Carbonates accumulate at the depth below the soil surface down to which the profile is frequently wetted. Progressively the calcium carbonate coats the surfaces of structural units and drainage channels, and later fills up the pore space within the soil matrix. Nodules of calcium carbonate grow gradually, pushing together soil particles and aggregates so that the bulk density of the horizon is increased. When the

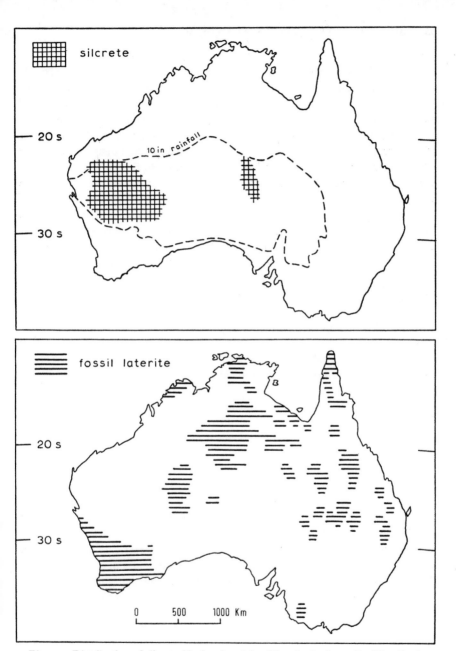

Fig 3:5 Distribution of silcrete (duripan) and fossil laterite in Australia. The distributions are partly complementary, indicating different formative conditions on opposite sides of the present 10 in (250 mm) isohyet. Silcrete map adapted from Litchfield and Mabbutt (1962) and laterite from Prescott and Pendleton (1952)

nodules finally join up, almost all the pore space is filled with calcium carbonate and downward passage of soil solutions is very much reduced or halted altogether. Soil water then moves laterally over the surface of the hardened petrocalcic or caliche horizon, which is called *kunkar* in Australia. Evaporation of this water results in the build-up of the caliche by superimposed laminations of calcium carbonate. This capping layer is the hardest and densest part of the caliche. The amount of calcium carbonate required to form a cemented horizon varies according to the amount of surface to be coated and pore space to be filled. Clay-rich soils require a large amount while a relatively small amount of calcium carbonate will fill up a sandy or gravelly horizon so that it becomes hardened. Analytical data show that petrocalcic horizons have at least 40 per cent weight calcium carbonate in the mineral fraction when the stage of cementation to hardness is reached. Often the proportion is much greater and may be supplemented by calcium and aluminium silicates which contribute to the hardening.

Cementation by sesquioxides of iron and aluminium is associated with pedogenesis in humid environments, but over a wide range of temperature conditions from the tropics to high latitudes. The scale and form of sesquioxide cementation is variable from thin iron pan crusts in podsols to thick vesicular laterite or plinthite horizons in tropical red soils, and consequently, several processes are thought to be involved in the movement and hardening of sesquioxides. The formation of plinthite in tropical soils seems to depend on fluctuations of the water table level. Groundwater is the solution carrying dissolved iron in a reduced state, and this is later oxidised to ferric oxide when the level falls. As part of this process, a pale or 'pallid' horizon is developed below the plinthite. Eventually the accumulation of sesquioxides brought in by the rise of groundwater, lateral drainage and by leaching from upper parts of the profile is distributed through most of the pore space of an illuvial horizon to produce a continuous, cellular structure. The walls of ferric oxide harden irreversibly on drying while the light coloured aluminium oxide and clay minerals remain soft. The hardening and cementing by ferric oxide depends on its developing a crystalline structure. Frequent wetting and drying, which may also remove other soil constituents while promoting a higher density and crystalline structure of iron oxide, is necessary to develop the hardening of plinthite. Investigation has shown that the skeleton of clay minerals remaining in the plinthite are of the stable, non-elastic 1:1 type such as kaolinite or gibbsite which provides an unchanging matrix on which the crystalline plinthite grows.

Iron and aluminium sesquioxides may combine with organic matter to cement ortstein which is a water-stable part of B horizons in podsols. Aluminium and organic matter are always in the cement of ortstein, but iron and manganese oxides may or may not be present. A distinct and continuous crust of ferric oxide—an iron pan—usually no more than one centimetre thick, is the product of a similar type of cementation in freely draining, leached soils. It is formed as part of the podsolisation process and its highly variable thickness, depth from the surface, and morphology are related to variation in its pedogenic conditions. The iron pan always has the same position within a soil profile, between the depleted A_e or albic horizon and the spodic B horizon, but may reoccur in the parent material as a product of geomorphological rather than pedogenic processes. So thin is the cemented iron pan and so complex can be its morphology in three dimensions that it may outline units of the albic A_e horizon in both vertical and horizontal planes through the soil body (see photograph, page 89). The iron pan is a precipitate of ferric oxide which is formed wherever the iron concentration increases sufficiently to take the iron compounds out of a metal-saturated solution.

Irreversible hardening of sesquioxide-rich horizons does not appear to be dependent on a certain proportion being present in the soil, but primarily on the complete covering of the surface of clay minerals by iron oxide. Sesquioxides in excess of this requirement can form a crystalline structure on drying. Cementation by aluminium oxide appears to be possible, in ortsteins for example, without drying. Plinthite cementation may be possible with as little as 10 per cent of the mineral materials as iron in ferric oxide while other soils may not be cemented with over 25 per cent iron or 36 per cent ferric oxide. Ten per cent as iron may be sufficient where the soil is sandy and coarse textured, with a relatively small proportion of clay minerals. Generally, the proportions of sesquioxides found in cemented horizons are intermediate between the very low proportions of silica and the very high proportions of calcium carbonate that have to be present to create the same effect of hardening.

Sesquioxide hardening is encouraged where clay minerals are minimal in quantity and of an inert type, while silica cementation is found on all types of clay minerals and only partially modifies their characteristics of swelling and shrinking. The variety of these formative circumstances emphasises the range of pedogenic conditions in which soil pans can develop.

Fragipans present yet another type of development and pan composition. They are exceptional among other soil pans because they lack any great quantity of cement and occur at the base of the solum. Fragipans have been studied in America and have also been the object of investigations in Scotland, particularly by E. A. FitzPatrick (1956) and J. C. C. Romans (1962). These two authors disagree about the origin of fragipans in podsolic soils, but both would accept the diagnostic properties of these indurated horizons. Fragipans may be of variable thickness (10–30 cm) usually with a smooth, sharply defined upper surface. They are brittle when handled and have a platy structure. They have a high bulk density and a pore space of less than 25 per cent. Fragipans contain little clay or any translocated compound, except possibly alumina. The compacted horizons usually occur more than 40 cm from the soil surface. Fitz-Patrick has explained fragipans of the lower part of freely draining humid-temperate soils as an inheritance from pedogenesis in a periglacial climate at the end of the last Pleistocene glaciation. He considers they are the product of freeze-thaw activity in permafrost, and consequently are relict features in their present situations. Romans quotes evidence from eastern Scotland to show that fragipans can be produced in the contemporary development of podsols, and ascribes their origin to contemporary pedogenic rather than periglacial processes. It seems that both explanations are acceptable and should be considered in relation to the respective field evidence on which they are based. Fragipans may be either fossil or current features of freely draining profiles— usually acid and podsolised. They are indurated by pressure interlocking coarse particles and only cemented by small quantities of translocated alumina among the clay minerals.

Soil as a three-dimensional medium is both an environment and product of the environment. Soil formation processes so far considered in general terms must now be discussed with specific reference to type profiles in the next chapter. It is essential that the three-dimensional framework be understood. Although it is an unfamiliar concept to many and presents difficulties of measurement and visual representation, the three dimensions of the soil body are its primary property which affects all others and all soil processes. Field examination of soil morphology depends on this premise; it is part of the basic procedure of the spatial selection of soil inspection points prior to soil mapping, amplified in Chapter 8. Soil formation processes should be introduced to the reader in this context, and then illustrated by association with soil profile types. The most convincing demonstration of the three-dimensional medium is in surface soil horizons such as the cultivated epipedon, or strongly coloured sub-surface horizons or those pan horizons that have been cemented to hardness. These are horizons in which the three dimensions register forcibly with the senses of the observer and areal limits are as noticeable as the vertical. They are the pedogenic products of a three-dimensional medium.

Bibliography

BALLANTYNE, A. K. Recent accumulation of salts in the soils of Southeastern Saskatchewan, *Canadian Journal of Soil Science*, 43 (1963), 52–58.

BLOOMFIELD, C. A study of podzolization, *Journal of Soil Science*, 4 (1953), 5–16, 17–23, and 5 (1954), 39–45, 46–49, 50–56, and 6 (1955), 284–92.

CROWTHER, E. M. The sceptical soil chemist, *Journal of Soil Science*, 4 (1953), 1–22.

FITZPATRICK, E. A. An indurated soil horizon formed by permafrost, *Journal of Soil Science*, 7 (1956), 248–54.

FITZPATRICK, E. A. Some aspects of soil evolution in north-east Scotland, *Soil Science*, 107 (1969), 403–8.

FLACH, K. W. *et al.* Pedocementation: induration by silica, carbonates and sesquioxides in the Quaternary, *Soil Science*, 107 (1969), 442–53.

JENNY, H. Role of the plant factor in pedogenic functions, *Ecology*, 39 (1958), 5–16.

LITCHFIELD, W. H. and MABBUTT, J. A. Hardpan in soils of semi-arid western Australia, *Journal of Soil Science*, 13 (1962), 148–59.

McKEAGUE, J. A. and ST ARNAUD, R. J. Pedotranslocation: eluviation-illuviation in soils during the Quaternary, *Soil Science*, 107 (1969), 428–34.

PRESCOTT, J. A. and PENDLETON, R. L. *Laterite and lateritic soils*, Commonwealth Agricultural Bureau, 1952.

ROMANS, J. C. C. Some measurements of air space in Scottish soils, *Journal of Soil Science*, 10 (1959), 201–14.

ROMANS, J. C. C. The origin of the indurated B3 horizon of podzolic soils in north-east Scotland, *Journal of Soil Science*, 13 (1962), 141–47.

SCHNITZER, M. and SKINNER, S. I. M. Organo-metallic interactions in soil, *Soil Science*, 96 (1963), 181–86.

SOIL SURVEY STAFF, *Soil classification—a comprehensive system*, 7th Approximation, US Dept of Agriculture, Washington, 1960.

CHAPTER FOUR

Soil Profiles and Soil-forming Environments

Introduction: the recognition and sub-division of soil profiles

THERE ARE SOME DISADVANTAGES IN TAKING THE SOIL PROFILE AS REPRESENTATIVE of the genetic characteristics of the whole soil body. While a vertical section is preferable to one taken at any other angle, the soil body does not develop perfectly horizontal and uniform horizons, amenable everywhere to vertical section sampling. This is apparent in any extended soil profile, such as found along a quarry face, road cutting, or drainage ditch, where variation is exposed both in thickness and composition of what are regarded as the same horizons. Necessarily, pedological opinion has moved in favour of the three-dimensional pedon as the more realistic unit of representation of the soil body, reflecting more closely its complexity as well as its stage and mode of formation. Despite this trend in pedological thought, the vertical section of the soil profile is the most easily demonstrated expression of the soil body and still serves as the best teaching model for introducing the study of soil in the field. In any case, it has been argued in the previous chapter that there is only a marginal difference between the profile and pedon as soil units. Some of the disadvantages involved with the profile may be overcome if care is taken not to claim that it is representative of more than its immediately surrounding soil body. Closely spaced inspection holes should be dug and sample profiles compared before claims can be made for a greater area of even relative uniformity.

The soil profile is used to examine both weathering and pedogenesis. A prepared section should be made as deep as the penetration of these processes, except where excessive depth, such as in tropical areas, makes it impractical. The profile should include at least part of the parent material from which it has developed, and this may require an inspection pit or section to 1·5 m or more in depth. In areas of embryonic soils, all horizons of the profile may be present within 0·5 m of the surface, and even in a glaciated landscape 1 m depth may be sufficient. The parent material is identified by a visible decrease in the degree of physical and chemical weathering compared with the horizons of the solum above. It may be physically consolidated as in rock, or if unconsolidated as in a transported deposit, the parent material will probably be the most compacted and least highly coloured by oxidation of all the horizons in the profile. It is not always an easily identified horizon especially where none of the other horizons is highly coloured so that there is little visible horizon differentiation in the profile. However, the first fact to establish in any examination of a soil profile is the junction between the parent material and the more weathered horizons of the solum above, which are altered by pedogenesis.

After establishing the depth of the profile, the soil surveyor must decide the profile type as the second point. It is suggested that the beginner in soil geography should follow a simple guide of classifying the soil profile into one of two primary types, namely whether it is freely drained or not (see Fig 4:1). The approach is, of course, a genetic one, but however unfashionable that may be on the current frontiers of pedological thought, it is useful at an introductory level, especially to encourage the understanding of soil development on a local scale. The field study of soils for most students is limited to a relatively small area, probably at most their own country, so that the range of soil profiles they may encounter is small enough to be contained by a simple genetic classification. On an international scale, it has been found more profitable to correlate soil profile similarities on the basis of specifically defined properties of horizons —an approach too complex and exact for an introductory study. The division between freely draining and poorly draining profiles is established by the maximum (ie, upper) level reached by the groundwater table, which is identified in the field by the boundary between the bright and uniform coloration of completely oxidised mineral compounds above and the mottled appearance of mixed oxidised and reduced compounds below and within the fluctuation zone of the groundwater table. Freely drained profiles have their water table down in the parent material horizon, and even if several horizons occur above, each will be almost uniformly oxidised. Profiles not freely draining, or having impeded drainage to some degree, may have the top part of the profile above

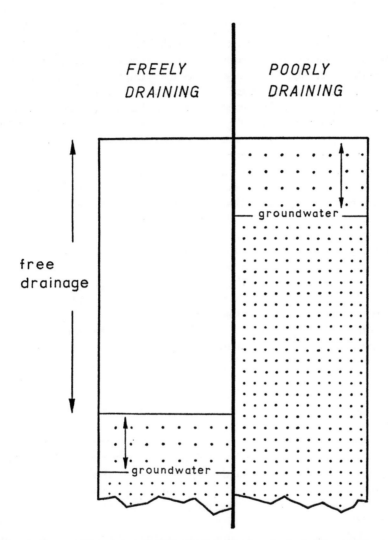

Fig 4:1   One possible primary division of soil profiles into freely draining and poorly
draining types

the maximum reach of the water table. Because, in this case, the water table fluctuates in a zone above the parent material, the soil profile is regarded as imperfectly or poorly drained even if surface horizons are locally well drained. Where the water table frequently reaches the soil surface or plant litter zone, the soil profile will be very poorly drained and periodically waterlogged. This rise of the water table excludes air from the soil pore space and so prohibits oxidation of weathered mineral products. Where part or all the soil profile is subjected to changes of water table, the result is a patchwork of rusty and grey mottling in the fluctuation zone, and beneath this, or below the minimum water table level, there is an absence of rust, orange, or red colours.

Having made the distinction between freely draining soils and those that are not, it should be emphasised that the latter category includes a considerable range of soil profiles. However, the important and basic difference is this two-fold one, and the two categories of soil profile are to be found in any area, large or small, in any environment of the earth's surface. The aim here is to select some easily identified features that reflect soil genesis and that can be seen anywhere. They can be used as guidelines for any local, introductory study of soils in the field. Among soils of partly to completely impeded drainage, variety can be seen in different soil profile types according to their genesis, and the actual soil property values of the same soil profile type can vary from one soil-forming environment to another. Specific and precise values of horizon differentiation belong to the advanced study of soils, and at an introductory level it is sufficient to concentrate on the main field characteristics of horizons.

After the first two stages of identification of profile limits and type, attention should be given thirdly to soil profile features. Soil horizons, differentiated by pedogenesis, must now be grouped into parent material and those of the more weathered mineral and organic horizons of the solum above. Conventionally, the latter have been known as A and B horizons, the parent material being C, and any deeply buried, unrelated material known as the D horizon. The A horizons are the most weathered, usually humus-rich surface horizons, and possibly depleted of leachable compounds; the B horizons, if present, occupy the middle position and are enriched with compounds from the A horizons above. Both can be sub-divided into many component horizons some of which are diagnostic of particular pedogenic conditions and hence soil profile type.

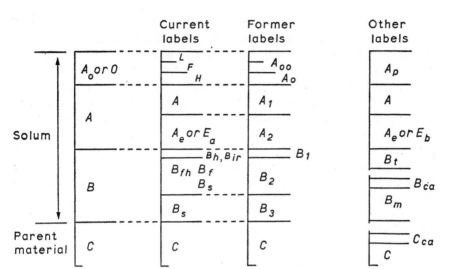

Fig 4:2 Soil horizon nomenclature for freely draining soil profiles. Where these horizons occur in gleys, they carry the suffix letter g

Ao L	—fresh organic litter
F	—partly decomposed litter
H	—black, jelly-like humus
A, A, or A_1	—mixed organo-mineral horizon near surface
Ap	—ploughed, cultivated organo-mineral surface horizon
Ae, Ea, or A_2	—leached, acid horizon
Ae or Eb	—eluviated basic or slightly acid horizon

B, Bh	—humus enriched illuvial horizon
Bir	—iron cemented pan
Bf	—horizon strongly enriched with oxidised iron
Bfh	—horizon enriched with iron and humus
Bs	—horizon enriched by translocated sesqui-oxides of iron and aluminium
Bt	—textural B horizon with illuvial clay
Bm	—chemically weathered horizon enriched only with water-soluble salts
Bca, Cca	—calcium cemented horizons

The main types of soil profile are identified by the specific arrangement of horizons that each can contain. The A, B, C, and D horizon labels were introduced by the Russians in the early years of pedological research (around 1880–1900), and since the 1920s, have been widely used internationally. They are still commonly used in soil textbooks and soil survey reports, despite the current trend to re-name soil horizons. Recently, there have been several attempts to establish new soil horizon and profile nomenclature, none of them so near universal acceptance as those by the US Soil Survey in their 7th Approximation comprehensive soil classification. The American horizon names will be linked to the A, B, C, and D system in the following discussion, but the latter traditional labels are expected to be used for many years more and have merit as a conceptual framework for the beginner. Even if mistakes are made in its field application, the A, B, C, D system provides a complete scheme of soil horizon possibilities based on our current understanding of soil genesis. It has been strongly criticised in academic circles because of this very quality, ie, that it is designed to fit preconceived ideas about soil genesis which may yet be disproved. While this is fair criticism in that advances in pedology ought to be devising new classifications on the heels of new research findings, communication of ideas through textbooks changes slowly and usually follows well established, commonly used theory. Hence, one can justify this compromise policy, of being cautious towards the almost universally accepted 7th Approximation soil classification. The diagram (Fig 4:2) gives the full range of A, B, and C horizons that can occur in a soil profile, and in the next section the reader is provided with definitions of horizons used as diagnostic features for the ten soil orders of the US 7th Approximation comprehensive soil classification. These will be related to appropriate soil profiles in the following sections.

Definitions of some diagnostic horizons (7th Approximation, August 1960).

Diagnostic surface horizons (epipedons) which are examples of A horizons.

Mollic epipedon—A$_o$, thick, dark surface layer dominantly saturated with bivalent cations, with a low C/N ratio and moderate to strong structure.

Anthropic epipedon—A$_p$, similar to mollic epipedon in all respects except that it contains more than 250 ppm acid-soluble phosphate, formed by long continued systems of farming.

(*Above*) A shallow podsol on scree, disturbed by frost action, at high elevation in the Rockies, British Columbia; (*below*) frost sorting of material at an Arctic site has produced an almost ahumic soil that would be regarded as a Polar Desert profile (at the transition from an Entisol to an Inceptisol) (see page 113)

Plaggen epipedon—Ap, a man-made surface layer more than 50 cm thick—characteristics depend upon virgin epipedon from which it was originally derived.

Histic epipedon—Ao, thin surface horizon, saturated with water for some part of the year, high in organic carbon.

Diagnostic sub-surface horizons—which are B horizons, except for the albic or Ae horizon.

Argillic horizon—Bt illuvial horizon in which silicate clays have accumulated to a significant extent, ie, it has been clay-enriched by translocation.

Natric horizon—Bt/Bsa, an argillic horizon with prismatic or columnar structure, saline, having more than 15 per cent saturation with exchangeable sodium.

Spodic horizon—Bs/Bf/Bh/Bfh, illuvial accumulation of free sesquioxides, accompanied by organic matter; illuvial accumulation of iron oxides not accompanied by equivalent amounts of crystalline clay or illuvial accumulation of organic matter.

Cambic horizon—Bm, a changed or altered horizon, with formation of structure, liberation of iron oxides, formation of silicate clays, or obliteration of most evidence of original rock structure.

Oxic horizon—Bf, one from which weathering has removed or altered a large part of the silica combined with iron and aluminium, but not necessarily the quartz or 1:1 lattice clays, giving a concentration of clay-size minerals consisting of sesquioxides and 1:1 lattice silicate clays.

Calcic horizon—Bca, horizon of secondary carbonate enrichment not less than 15 cm thick, with calcium carbonate equivalent of more than 15 per cent usually with identifiable secondary carbonates as concretions or powder.

Albic horizon—Ae, horizon from which clay and free iron oxides have been removed, or in which oxides have been segregated to the extent that the colour of the horizon is determined by the primary sand and silt rather than by coatings on these particles.

The ten soil orders of the American 7th Approximation, arranged in the order of discussion in the following sections.

Entisols—embryonic mineral soils without profile development.

(*Left*) A freely draining brown earth without any visible soil horizons and having a well developed crumb structure; (*right*) a rendzina soil profile (A C horizons) on chalk in the Chiltern Hills, SE England. The A horizon is composed of organic matter and shattered chalk (see page 115)

G

Inceptisols—soils with weakly developed horizons; young soils that may be inhibited or regenerated in their development.

Alfisols—leached, basic or slightly acid soils with a diagnostic B$_t$ (clay-enriched) horizon.

Spodosols—leached acid soils with a spodic B horizon.

Ultisols—deeply weathered, leached acid soils.

Oxisols—very deeply weathered, highly leached acid soils with a diagnostic oxic horizon.

Mollisols—soils with a diagnostic surface mollic horizon, humic and rich in bivalent ions (calcium and magnesium).

Aridisols—saline and alkaline mineral soils of desert environments.

Vertisols—disturbed and inverted clay soils.

Histosols—organic soils.

Some soil profiles and their environmental range. Modern pedology was founded on the concept that certain commonly found soil profiles were associated with particular regions or zones of climate. Hence these soil profiles were known as zonal soils, based on what was called the 'concept or principle of zonality'. Apart from being an over-simplification of reality, the zonal system had the unfortunate effect of restricting, in the mind of the student, the distribution of each zonal soil within the limits of its climatic zone. Such a distortion of the truth was a most imperfect way of introducing soil geography and led to the formation of fixed ideas difficult to remove. It is preferable to adopt the diametrically opposed view that the infinite possibilities for the development of soil profiles means prediction is difficult, sometimes impossible for the field surveyor. Secondly, it must be said that there is only limited regional association in the world distribution of type profiles or *great soil groups*. It is true that there are loosely defined bio-climatic regions of the world where these representative profiles are regarded as dominant because they are commonly recurrent when viewed over a large area. But, within any small part of these regions, the type of profile may not be dominant; as the zonal soils were almost always freely draining profiles, local dominance is unlikely. The zonality concept might have worked if the earth's surface had been a level and freely draining plain, but this is patently not so and uneven terrain produces more exceptions than the rule. Variation of climate and vegetation with relief and altitude means that most soil-forming environments are recurrent in their world distribution. Certainly the cold and cool environments, both humid and arid, can be found in low latitude tropical areas at high altitude. Therefore, the great variety of soils usually associated with these climatic environments do also occur in tropical highlands, so that their general world distribution is from the equator almost to the Poles. Probably the most restricted in distribution are the soils of tropical lowlands, soils which are the result of many millions of years of humid, high temperature weathering and pedogenesis. Their actual distribution covers a significant proportion of the earth's surface, but the conditions required for their pedogenesis means that these *latosols* or *ferralitic soils* (known as *Oxisols*) are not found in middle and high latitude environments. At an early stage of soil investigation, the student should adopt a mental framework to accommodate what might appear to be a contradiction, ie, *that lowland tropical soils have an extensive actual distribution but a limited world range, the reverse being true of other soils.*

In the following discussion, it is proposed to follow the highest categories of the US 7th Approximation—the ten orders—as a guide for the soil profiles examined, but also to include some regional appreciation of soil profile distribution. This is not to embrace the old zonal concept, but rather to emphasise the variation of soil profiles to be found within any region. This is true even of landscapes with the least potential to develop soils, namely the Arctic tundra.

Cold environment soils (Entisols and Inceptisols). This environment (Arctic tundra) is the extreme contrast to the tropical lowlands, being constrained both in the total length of time since glaciation as well as in annual season time that weathering and pedogenesis is possible. The tropics have enjoyed millions of years, since Tertiary geological time, of almost unbroken and undisturbed soil formation. Most parts of the Arctic tundra have been ice-free for no more, and often less, than a few thousands of years, and for only a very brief period of six to ten weeks in those years has soil formation taken place. Nevertheless, such minimal soil development is expressed in variety and not uniformity within small sample areas. As with the plant composition in the tundra, soils may be variable over short distances, depending largely on the depth of permafrost, but are relatively uniform over the vast total area of this environment. Tundra soils are important because no less than 20 per cent of the earth's surface is underlain by permafrost and most of this is within the Arctic tundra (Fig 4:3).

In the tundra, all the soil-forming factors are present in minimal measure. Generally, there is little range of relief, most of the landscape being a monotonous plain and strongly influenced by the presence of permafrost. Climate and vegetation do not encourage soil formation, there being less than three

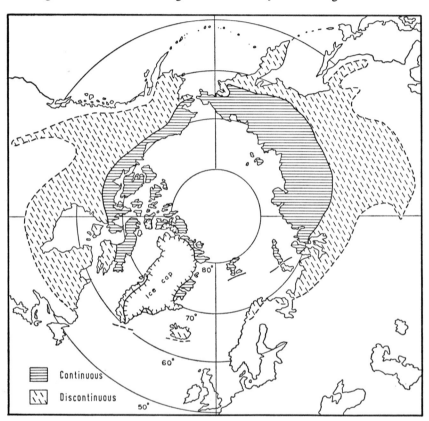

Fig 4:3   Distribution of continuous and discontinuous permafrost in the northern hemisphere (after Black, 1954)

months of the year when plant growth and soil-forming processes are possible. Parent material variation can provide contrasts, but to some extent these are modified by limited weathering and total depth of soil. The tundra is climatically arid, the mean annual rainfall usually being less than 250 mm, and much of the soil moisture in early summer comes from thawing of the permafrost. Plant cover may often be discontinuous, and climate reduces the amount of vegetable production as well as the rate of organic decay.

The Arctic tundra is usually sub-divided into two parts, the more arid Polar Desert environment and the southern, peripheral, and more humid tundra grassland. In the former, the essential character of the soil-forming environment is similar to that of any desert. Very little moisture is available from the atmosphere, less than 130 mm annually, and plant distribution is only occasional or sporadic. In the short, warm season of the Polar Desert, soil moisture is attracted upwards and requires to move by capillary attraction only a short distance to the drying soil surface. Permafrost is always less than 70 cm from the surface; the thickness of the thawed 'active' layer decreases poleward and with increasing moisture content. Very commonly in the Polar Desert environment, the 'active' layer is only 25 cm deep so that a surface efflorescence of sodium and calcium salts from the soil is quite common. Plants cover less than 25 per cent of the surface, and soil fauna being much less numerous than in other soils, the organic component hardly enters the soil formation system. Soils contain few weathered minerals, and are usually gravelly or sandy in composition. The Polar Desert soil is classified as an Inceptisol. Other soils are so shallow and stony that they are regarded as lithosols, and are only at an embryonic stage of soil development (known as Entisols in the 7th Approximation). There is no visible sign of horizon development in these profiles, but the thawed soil is called an A horizon. Entisols are discussed later in a separate section as they have a very wide global distribution.

Outward and southward from the Arctic deserts, the fringing tundra grasslands provide conditions slightly more conducive to weathering and profile development. On freely drained sites, the thawed soil in summer can be 2 m or more in depth. A complete and dense plant cover contributes humus and organic acids for leaching of freely draining profiles. Locally, where such conditions are found, slightly leached brown earth profiles develop (called

Arctic brown earths), but more often the permafrost basement impedes soil drainage. Moisture held in the soil encourages the growth of plants in an otherwise arid environment, and in turn the denser plant cover produces humus which further increases the moisture-holding capacity of the soil. The highly organic or peaty soils that result are among the most shallow 'active' profiles when the summer thaw arrives. The high moisture content of these soils reduces the effective depth of thaw and this leads to the accumulation of organic debris. These shallow, waterlogged, and highly organic soils are popularly called bog soils, otherwise Histosols of the 7th Approximation. The freely draining soils of both tundra grassland and Polar Desert are known as Inceptisols, in common with a variety of soils from other environments that display little sign of horizon development. In the tundra grassland, processes of organic decay and leaching operate still at minimal rate and degree; where leaching can take place, it normally reaches only the early decalcification stage. Because of this, soil pH values are high (pH 5·0–8·0 even in the surface horizons) and *base saturation* is high despite the small size of the *base exchange capacity*. Slow organic decay inhibits the natural supply of nitrogen and phosphorus in the soil so that plant life responds dramatically to enrichment from these nutrients around present and past settlement sites. Tundra soils have little or no agricultural potential because of these nutrient and physical deficiencies, as well as related climatic limitations.

Inceptisols, so common in the tundra, are also found in other environments. In the zonal classification of soils, based as it was on soil-forming conditions rather than on soil characteristics, no affinity is recognised between the soils of the tundra and others of lower latitude environments. Among Inceptisols which show only weak horizonation, the 7th Approximation includes brown earths and associated gleys, usually located in mid-latitude humid and sub-humid environments. They are genetically similar to tundra soils in that the freely draining soils of both groups are the product of only an early stage of leaching. They are decalcified and even acidified, but their genesis has not reached the stage of translocation of sesquioxides and clay. Inceptisols are even found in the tropics, but only on the exceptional parent materials of volcanic ash and lavas, alluvium, and other deposits of recent origin. The 7th Approximation allows us to group together soils from a variety of bioclimatic environments which, by different circumstances, have reached a similar stage in pedogenesis. The distinction among them probably lies in their future or potential development. Although not known for certain, the potential development of Inceptisols in the tropics, both in weathering and pedogenesis, is much greater than for tundra soils under their prevailing climate in the same time period. However, the probable or improbable future is not relevant to the classification of contemporary soils, and the important point is that in any part of the world Inceptisols reflect only the inception of leaching. It is recognised that their profile development is more advanced than the Entisols (= lithosols), but less than other soils.

Brown earths (Inceptisols). Brown earths, mentioned earlier as members of the Inceptisols, are soil profiles of immense agricultural potential. They occur widely throughout the long settled lands in Western Europe and eastern North America (as well as in the other continents) so the brown earths have a history of cultivation and pedological investigation. Their name is derived from 'braunerde', first used by the German pedologist Ramann in 1905 and reintroduced by Kubiena in 1948. Between these dates, there had developed some divergence of interpretation about the braunerde or brown earth, and a number of new terms were introduced to describe this soil profile type. The divergence has continued to the present so that *sol brun acide* (France), brown forest soil (USA and Canada) and brown earth (UK) all refer to the same or very similar profile first described by the Germans as braunerde. It is freely draining and well weathered, shows oxidised mineral compounds but has no visible illuvial horizon in an A (B) C arrangement of horizons. This profile type may be decalcified and acidified without reaching the stage of movement of sesquioxides of iron and aluminium (see Fig 4:4).

Equally the brown earths include variations having a high base status as in the profiles *sol brun* and *sol brun calcaire* (France), brown calcareous soils and brown earths of high base status (UK), or eutrophic braunerde (Kubiena, 1953) as in Fig 4:5. The extremes of these calcareous conditions are the limestone soils, rendzina and terra rossa, which could be either Inceptisols or Mollisols. The brown earth profile is almost uniform in its appearance and properties from the soil surface to its parent material. As the brown earth closely reflects the colour and the character of its parent material, it is not

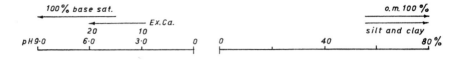

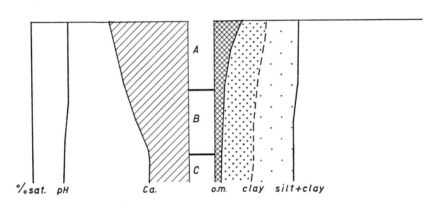

BROWN EARTH

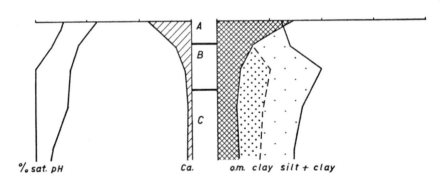

BROWN EARTH

Fig 4:4   Brown earth profile examples of Inceptisols. (*Above*) Soil developed from basic igneous derived till in south-east Scotland; (*below*) soil developed from ultra-basic till at a site near Aberdeen, Scotland (key opposite)

necessarily brown; red marls and red sandstones develop brown earths that are uniformly red or reddish-brown. The gradual decrease of organic matter down the profile, decay and incorporation being encouraged by the aeration of the soil, contributes to its uniform appearance. Brown earths can maintain these features of incipient leaching because the mobilisation process is inhibited by lack of organic leachate solution, as well as by the replenishment of any leached cations from chemical weathering of the mineral reserves. Leaching, and in particular the mobilisation of sesquioxides and clay minerals, is resisted by the local combination of soil-forming factors. For these reasons, the brown earth is one of the most desirable soils for cultivation (Fig 4:6).

Alfisols. Brown earths, by definition, are at the starting point of several

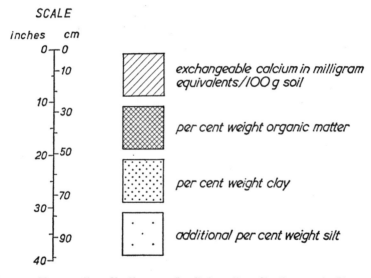

Fig 4:4a   Key to soil profile diagrams. In all the soil profile diagrams in Chapter 4, horizontal and vertical scales are kept uniform for comparisons to be made. The four shadings used are explained above. Per cent base saturation (% base sat.) is the measure of the proportion of the clay-humus colloid surface that is filled with exchangeable base ions (basic cations), rather than hydrogen ions. pH is related to % base sat.

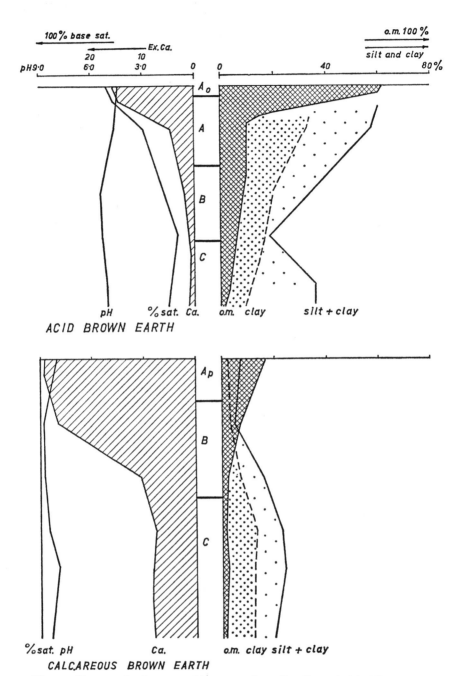

Fig 4:5 Extremes in the range of brown earth profiles (Inceptisols). (*Above*) Acid brown earth from shale till in the Southern Uplands; (*below*) Calcareous brown earth from coastal shelly sand in north-east Scotland

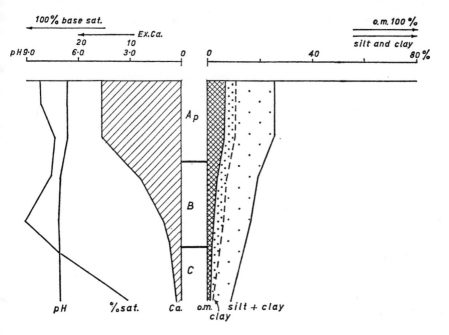

CULTIVATED BROWN EARTH

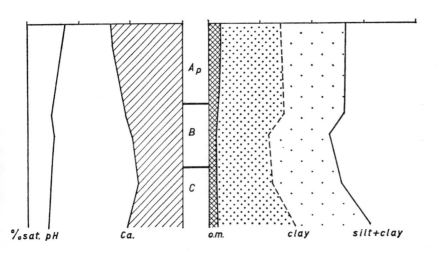

CULTIVATED BROWN EARTH

Fig 4:6   Cultivated brown earths (Inceptisols) with modified Ap horizons. (*Above*)
From glacio-fluvial sands derived from *Old Red Sandstone*; (*below*) from shale derived
from till—both in south-east Scotland

possible and divergent lines of profile development. If leaching becomes more effective, the acid–alkaline contrast, already established among brown earths, will become more marked, and acid conditions can lead to eventual podsolisation. On alkaline base-rich parent materials, weathering keeps pace with leaching and at least prevents acidification. After decalcification, the physical eluviation of silicate clay in these soils leads to the formation of a clay-enriched horizon, called B_t or 'textural B'. This is the argillic or natric (if sodium rich) horizon of the 7th Approximation, and the soil order is that of the Alfisols. These soils have grey or pale brown A_0 and A_e (Eb) surface horizons of medium base status, with good decay and incorporation of organic matter, which overlies an illuvial clay-rich B_t horizon. There is little colour change from one horizon to another, but a significant increase in the per cent clay (see Fig 4:7) in the argillic or B_t horizon. This is regarded as the diagnostic horizon of the Alfisols which include soil profiles otherwise known as grey-brown podsolics, *sol brun lessivé*, and grey-wooded soils. They develop on well-weathered parent materials of the last glaciation age and older, and are associated with humid and sub-humid, temperate and sub-tropical climates, eg, base-rich parent materials and nutrient-rich broadleaf tree or grassland vegetation help to sustain moderate alkalinity in the surface horizons against considerable leaching to form these soils. Consequently Alfisols are regarded as soils with a good to outstanding agricultural potential (see photograph on page 125).

Podsolised soils (Spodosols). Spodosols are soils with a spodic horizon, according to the 7th Approximation. The diagnostic spodic horizon is an illuvial accumulation of sesquioxides with or without organic matter, which lies under an A_e 'albic' or light coloured horizon. This order of soils includes all profiles that show signs of podsolisation, and in this way are distinguished from related Inceptisols and Alfisols. Previously, there existed the possibility of confusion by linking weakly podsolised soils with acid brown earths ('brown forest soil' has been used to describe both) and with grey-brown podsolics simply through name association. Spodosols isolate in one order all soils with the albic-spodic horizon combination, and also include poorly drained profiles with the diagnostic spodic horizon. Brown podsolics, podsols, peaty podsols, and groundwater podsols are the traditional names for profiles of the Spodosol order. They are associated with coniferous forest, heath, or other base-

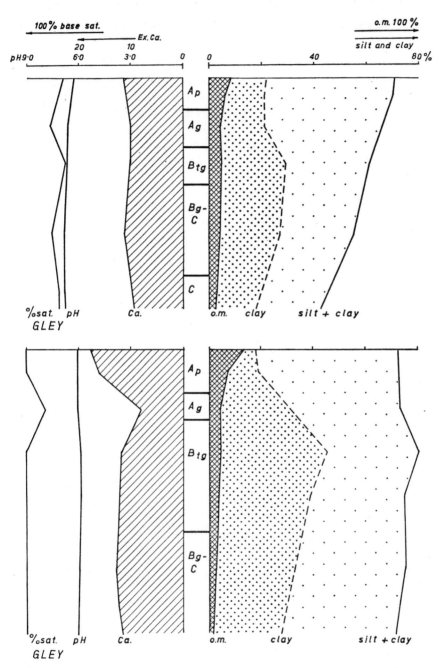

Fig 4:7 Grey-brown podsolics which have become gleyed by the presence of a B$_t$ horizon. They are regarded as gleys, but are also Alfisols, (Shropshire, England)

deficient vegetation, cool and cold humid climatic conditions, and parent materials that are acid and porous. In most cases, Spodosols are found where temperature conditions limit the period of weathering, plant growth and decay, and where excessive moisture in a freely draining soil encourages leaching. The main distribution area of spodosols or podsols is in the high latitude coniferous forests of North America and Eurasia where parent materials are usually glacial in origin. Podsols are most likely to develop where these are sandy, and therefore porous and base deficient.

In the early stages of podsolisation, there is a visible enrichment of the Bf or spodic horizon with free sesquioxides which distinguishes brown podsolic profiles from acid brown earths. The embryonic spodic horizon is identified by the slight rusty colour of ferric oxide, while there is a complementary loss of colour in the albic horizon above. It would be almost impossible otherwise to specify the free sesquioxides as moved from above rather than locally weathered (Fig 4:8). Podsolisation progresses further if the soil is affected by an increasingly acid leachate which creates more acid conditions in the leached A horizons, especially the Ae or albic horizon. Acidity in the surface mineral horizons inhibits decay of organic matter by encouraging fungal micro-organisms at the cost of bacteria. Cold temperatures, excessive wetness, and the chemical composition of needle-leaf and heath plant litter all encourage the accumulation of surface organic litter into raw mor humus and gradually into thicker peat. This trend is accompanied by increasing acidity and podsolisation in the mineral soil below.

Brown podsolics are distinguished from other podsols by their organic carbon being highest in the surface horizon and decreasing with depth, unlike most podsols which have a second maximum in the spodic or B horizon from translocated humus. pH values do not reach the extremes that can be found in other podsols, and likewise the per cent base saturation range is more moderate, not dropping to the low values of albic horizons in some podsols. Although brown podsolics are acid soils requiring lime and fertiliser treatment before cultivation, their characteristics of free drainage and good aeration give them a reasonably high agricultural potential. Their surface A horizons are usually so shallow and the Ae or albic horizon so faint that ploughing mixes and masks all horizons down to the spodic or B horizon.

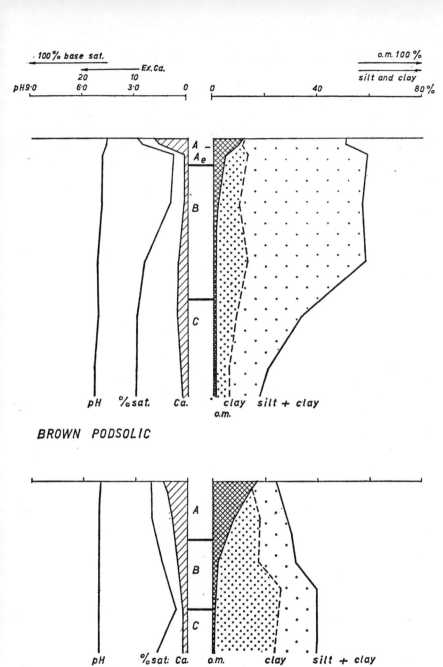

o.m. 100%

Ex. Ca.

silt and clay

pH9·0   6·0   3·0   0   0   40   80%

20   10

A –
Ae

B

C

pH   %sat.   Ca.   clay   silt + clay
o.m.

BROWN PODSOLIC

A

B

C

pH   %sat. Ca.   o.m.   clay   silt + clay

BROWN PODSOLIC

Fig 4:8   Two brown podsolic profiles, the upper one from New Haven, Conn, USA, and the lower from Galloway, south-west Scotland

Podsols are the ultimate stage of development for brown podsolics. There are many different types of podsol profile with no consistency in name; profile correlation among local names is a formidable task for pedologists. All podsols have horizon features that indicate progress through all the stages of leaching—decalcification, acidification, mobilisation and illuviation of the sesquioxides and clay-humus colloids—but the different types gain their distinctive characteristics from the scale and degree of podsolisation reached. Early in the sequence of stages in podsolisation, profiles called normal podsols or iron podsols show an obvious colour contrast between the albic (Ae) and spodic (Bf) horizons, the latter being visibly enriched with ferric oxide (see Fig 4:9). The rusty colour from the ferric oxide (aluminium oxides present do not add any colour) dominates and obscures the leached humus, which is in any case a subsidiary element at this stage in the podsolisation. Progressively the illuvial humus becomes more important and gradually blackens the rusty colour of the ferric oxide in the spodic horizon. Eventually a humus-iron or iron-humus podsol forms which has illuvial humus and sesquioxides as the spodic horizon. By this stage in podsolisation, the albic Ae horizon has become a structureless mass of quartz (silica) particles almost devoid of exchangeable bases, clay minerals, humus colloids, and sesquioxides (Fig 4:10). Its field expression is very clear with sharp well defined boundaries and a thickness of between 10 and 25 cm in most cases. Its whitish-grey colour may be darkly stained by humus being moved through the horizon, or perhaps simply as part of the drainage from the accumulating peat on the soil surface. The formation of the humus-iron podsol is associated with a wetter climatic environment than in the case of the iron podsols, and consequently with a greater scale of leaching producing thicker horizons in a deeper solum. Duchaufour (1960) has called them Atlantic podsols, and the iron podsols with a shallower solum and thinner horizons are Boreal podsols. The latter are found as coniferous forest soils in the drier, interior-continental parts, while the deeper Atlantic podsols usually develop with heath vegetation in wetter climate areas of British Columbia, the British Isles, and the rest of the northern Atlantic fringe of Europe.

Gleyed versions of spodosols are relatively common, both surface and groundwater gleying being found in the same areas as spodosols (Fig 4:11). Under particularly acid conditions and with the build-up of peat, podsols

(*Left*) Tropical ferralitic soil (Oxisol) in Zambia with its characteristic lack of surface organic matter and plinthite forming in a clayey horizon at the bottom of the pit (beside trowel); (*right*) grey-brown podsolic (Alfisol) profile developed on calcareous till near Hamilton, Ontario. The pale Ae or Eb horizon overlies the Bt horizon, their junction marked by the spade handle. The darker horizon below is the parent material (see page 120)

often develop a crust or pan of concentrated ferric oxide in the B horizon. This is produced in stages starting from an incipient phase and changing to a thick and consolidated layer up to 1 cm in thickness. In the extreme form, the iron pan is impervious and causes subsequent gleying in the Ae horizon above. These spodosols are called iron pan soils or peaty gleyed podsols with iron pan. Their iron pan is usually in the contact zone between the A and B horizons, but there may be exceptions both in profile position and in the three-dimensional form of the iron pan. In other cases, the humus-iron horizon becomes so dense and compacted that it too promotes surface water gleying in the A horizons. There are other examples of gleyed podsols in which the gleying is associated with the groundwater table and may not follow the formation of an impervious horizon. Groundwater podsols or hydromorphic podsols are examples. They are two part profiles, developing below wet and acid peat, and becoming thoroughly leached in their A horizons. The groundwater table and gleying is in the lower part of the profile, and because the soil water has moved through iron-rich mineral and organic matter, ferrous iron compounds are mobilised and later oxidised on the surface of the water table. This iron oxide horizon is a form of 'Bog Iron', and these groundwater podsols are often developed around peat bogs where the water table comes near or even reaches the surface of the mineral soil. In such sites, these soils can be a product of internal water movement.

Damman (1962) described what he called hydromorphic humus podsols in Newfoundland, Canada, that had developed below a peat bog in wet but reasonably freely draining mineral soil. Under such anaerobic conditions, there is no association between humus colloids and highly mobile ferrous iron. The latter is carried away in solution by the soil drainage, and only the humus remains to be deposited in the B horizon. These hydromorphic humus podsols can have approximately the same amount of humus in the B horizon as well-aerated humus-iron podsols, but the critical difference is that their anaerobic conditions exclude the possibility of iron deposition as well. From this example of a podsol, it is clear—as the original definition of spodosols allows—that iron and humus are contributory and not jointly necessary characteristics of the spodic horizon. It is certainly possible to have a spodic horizon without iron oxides, but there must be some translocated humus and aluminium oxide

(*Above*) A solonetz profile in South Australia showing strong prismatic structure in the B horizon indicated by the outstretched hand. A pale Ae or Eb horizon is found above; (*below*) organic gleys occupy wet hollows among drumlins of grey-brown podsolics near Hamilton, Ontario

H

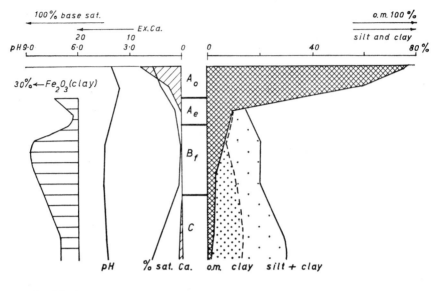

PODSOL

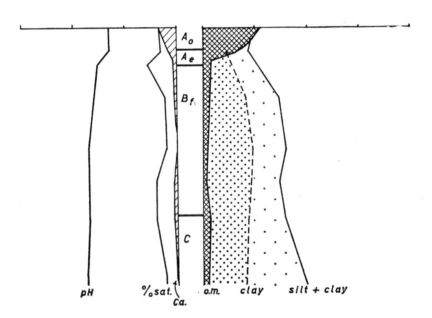

PODSOL

Fig 4:9 Podsols (Spodosols) from Scotland. (*Above*) Shale till in south-east Scotland; (*below*) Wellheads, near Fochabers, Morayshire

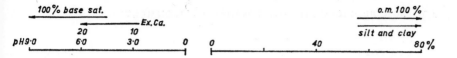

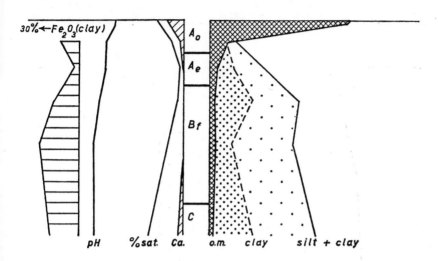

PEAT PODSOL

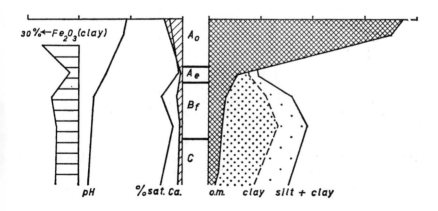

PEAT PODSOL

Fig 4:10 Peat podsols with mor humus and marked translocation of ferric oxide.
Both are developed on coarse sandstone till above 700 ft (210 m) in Scotland. (*Above*)
Tweed valley, Southern Uplands; (*below*) Upland Ayrshire

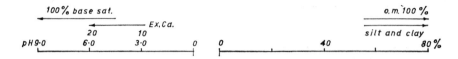

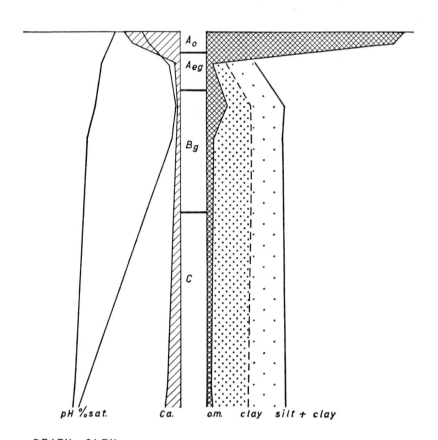

PEATY GLEY

Fig 4:11 Peaty gley profile which is also a Spodosol. It was developed on granitic
till at a site near Aberdeen, Scotland

present. The waterlogged conditions that promote the development of these partly or completely gleyed podsols also lead to the accumulation and expansion of surface peat bogs. These are a common feature of the level and swampy terrain found in the high-latitude coniferous forests of interior North America and Eurasia. They are associated particularly with level landscapes and those underlain by southern extensions of permafrost; under these site conditions, surface wetness and peat accumulation is encouraged, sometimes only locally but also covering large areas within the spodosol region.

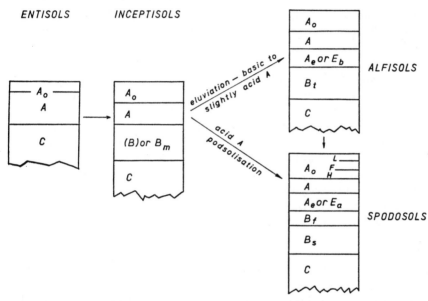

Fig 4:12   The relationship among Entisols, Inceptisols, Alfisols, and Spodosols—soils common in mid-latitude, humid environments

The diagrams in Fig 4:12 make the point that an evolutionary relationship exists among the Inceptisols, Spodosols, and Alfisols. The profiles of these three soil orders are affected to some degree by leaching and an evolution into another profile type is dependent on a change to a more intense stage of leaching. This may happen over time at one place with little change in soil-forming factors, or may be linked with an environmental change involving a different organic leachate or a greater degree of leaching. The base-rich grey-brown podsolics (Alfisols) develop in humid climates on relatively young and calcareous parent material, but even these may be chemically depleted in time to allow a change into an acid, podsolised profile. Under acid conditions, it is possible if not probable that acid brown earths (Inceptisols) will alter to podsols and even humus-iron podsols in time. Gleying, which is so characteristic of the spodosols, can occur in a number of ways at any stage in podsolisation.

Some soils of the tropics and subtropics (Ultisols and Oxisols). Ultisols and Oxisols—two more orders of the 7th Approximation—include soil profiles which are related by their common association with warm and hot, humid climates and consequently with intense chemical weathering and leaching. Soils of both orders are areally dominant in low and mid-latitude tropical and sub-tropical humid environments. In their geographical distribution, the Ultisols—otherwise known as red-yellow podsolics or ferruginous soils— merge into grassland soils on their arid margins and into Alfisols and Inceptisols (brown earths) on their cool humid margins (eg, in North America). Ultisols are regarded as more weathered and more acidic than Alfisols (grey-brown podsolics). They have the same clay-enriched (argillic) B horizons as the Alfisols, but the clay has a much lower degree of base saturation—usually less than 35 per cent. Ultisol profiles are much deeper than any others considered so far, with about 2 m of weathered solum, but despite their more advanced chemical weathering, these profiles still have a store of weatherable minerals. Their surface horizons are less acid than those of Spodosols, and in the well-drained, well-aerated state of many of their members, Ultisols make excellent agricultural soils with fertiliser application, as is the case in the eastern United States. Their silicate-clay minerals, only partly depleted of silica, exist along with non-silicate clays—ie, the sesquioxides of iron and aluminium. The latter contribute to the strong structural development of the soil and the iron gives distinctive colour to these red-yellow podsols. Some of the Ultisols in continental interiors become transitional with desert soils, while the order also includes high water table soils like humic gleys and groundwater laterite soils. In the latter, the B horizon, rich in ferric oxide and clay is supplied with reduced iron compounds in solution by the groundwater, and oxidation takes place at or above the groundwater surface. In general, the genesis of Ultisols, involves high temperatures and at least sub-humid conditions throughout the year. Weathering takes place all the time and leaching, through to podsolisation, may be either seasonal or continuous. Red-yellow podsolics have a pale Ae or albic horizon as in podsols, but their B horizon is a markedly clay-rich Bt as well as containing a high proportion of translocated humus and oxides of iron and aluminium. Yellow podsolics are wetter profiles with the iron compounds in a hydrated state; they are closely related to the gleys of the same environment. The red-yellow and red podsolics (Ultisols) are similar in general morphology and genesis to Oxisols of the humid tropics, but they have their own distinctive range of property values in their horizons (see Figs 4:13 and 4:14).

Oxisols are extensive throughout the humid tropics, but yet restricted to the lowlands of that environment. The freely drained profiles of the Oxisols are otherwise known as latosols, tropical red soils, or ferralitic soils (Figs 4:15 and 4:16). Many other types of soil profile may be found on exceptional parent materials and on exceptional sites in the tropics; it is not a domain exclusive to Oxisols as has been said earlier, but Oxisols are exclusive to the domain. They are soils with the diagnostic sub-surface horizon called an oxic horizon which has a concentration of clay-size minerals consisting of sesquioxides and 1:1 lattice silicate clays. Oxisols are also known as the soils with the greatest depth and intensity of chemical weathering due to the highly conducive climatic conditions of the humid tropics. The total solum is deep (up to 10 m) and horizons have a greater thickness than is found in soils of any other environment. Although there is a variety of soil profiles in the Oxisol order, all have the common properties of deep and advanced chemical weathering so that there are almost no weatherable minerals left, at least within the plant rooting zone. The Oxisols include gleyed profiles, but most are well drained soils that develop horizons with leaching through to podosolisation on a massive and spectacular scale. The result is that a complete Oxisol profile is basically similar to that of a Spodosol, with the qualification that the scale is much greater and that loss of surface horizons by erosion (truncation) is more common in Oxisols. Some of the chemical decomposition processes, such as the alteration

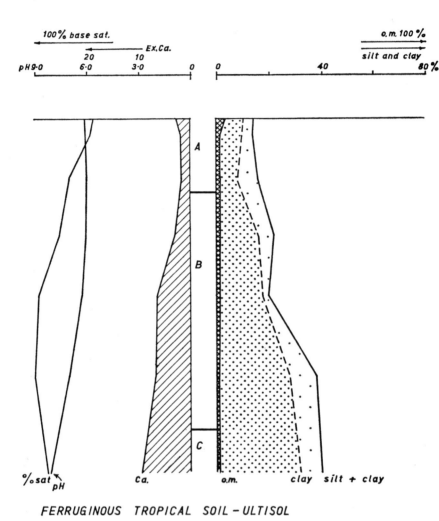

FERRUGINOUS TROPICAL SOIL – ULTISOL

Fig 4:13   Ferruginous tropical soil (Ultisol), developed from gneiss at a site in northern Nigeria

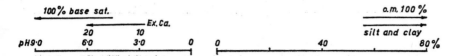

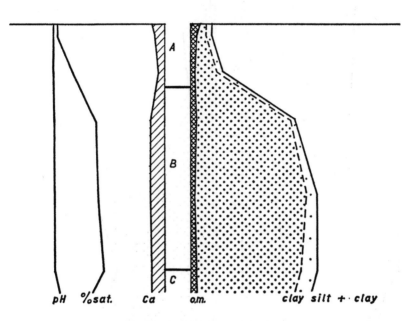

FERRUGINOUS TROPICAL SOIL - ULTISOL

Fig 4:14   Ferruginous tropical soil (Ultisol), developed from schist at a site in northern Nigeria. These soils are intermediate in reaction and have a particularly high clay content

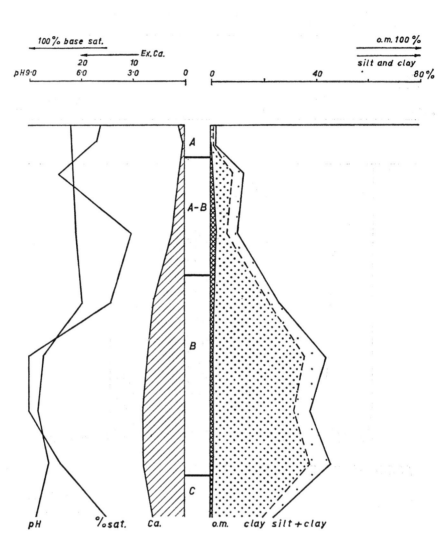

FERRUGINOUS SOIL WITH IRON CONCRETIONS — ULTISOL - OXISOL

Fig 4:15   Deeply weathered tropical soil with iron concretions in its B horizon (from northern Nigeria). It could be classed as an Ultisol or Oxisol

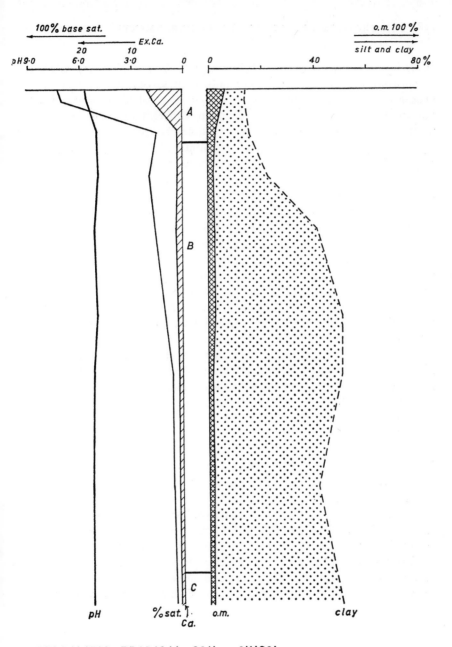

FERRALITIC TROPICAL SOIL - OXISOL

Fig 4:16 Ferralitic tropical soil (Oxisol) developed on gneiss in the Ivory Coast, West Africa. Note the depth of the solum

of 2:1 into 1:1 clays by the loss of silica, in podsols normally found only in the Ae horizon, are found in both A and B horizons in Oxisols. Both Spodosols and Oxisols have albic surface horizons, depleted of almost all leachable compounds, but are distinguished in their B horizons by different spodic or oxic characteristics. In Oxisols, there is no deposition of leached humus since rapid decay alters and reduces surface humus to a minimum. These soils are well known for their lack of soil organic matter and a store of associated nutrients such as nitrogen and phosphorus; consequently, Oxisols have to maintain a precarious balance in supplying the considerable nutrient demands of tropical forest plants against the ecological disintegration that would follow failure.

Although the bright red colour of their B horizons gives them a rich appearance and they support lush tropical vegetation, these soils are not agriculturally fertile. As has been said, they are quite acid, depleted of almost all weatherable and leachable compounds from surface horizons and almost lacking a surface organic horizon. If A horizons are present, they are pale brown in colour, shallow and composed mainly of quartz material resistant to weathering and leaching. The B horizons are deep and dominate the solum; there may be little else remaining if the plant and organic cover has been cleared for cultivation so encouraging the loss of the A horizon. The B horizon is an illuvial horizon into which are concentrated both leached and residual clays, mostly altered to 1:1 lattice silicate clays and translocated sesquioxides. The formation process is more fully discussed in the previous chapter. The clay fraction is composed mainly of kaolinite and ferric and aluminium oxides and hydroxides which may form plinthite or laterite at the top of the B horizon. The base exchange capacity and per cent base saturation of these 1:1 clays are low, and lower than in red-yellow podsolics. All plant nutrients are in short supply, particularly nitrogen and most of the phosphorus is in a fixed form, unavailable to plants.

The argillic sub-soil horizon Bt of red-yellow podsolics is not common in tropical red soils. It is reported to be present in the tropics where the dry season is more than two months, and parent material is young and only moderately weathered. In the humid equatorial areas, advanced weathering and loss of silica from the silicate clays to considerable depth reduces translocation by almost excluding the chance of clay eluviation within the top

2 m. Clay accumulation in Oxisols is located low in the solum, below the oxic horizon enriched by sesquioxides, and is often the cause of raising the level of groundwater gleying. The aquic or hydromorphic oxisols can be developed by such high water table conditions, ferrous oxide in solution being moved to and oxidised at the surface of the groundwater. Thus, ferric oxide crusts may be formed near the soil surface and overlie clay of the 2:1 lattice type. These hydromorphic Oxisols have high base exchange capacities and per cent saturation from their 2:1 clays (in contrast with freely draining, leached Oxisols), and are chemically fertile while presenting considerable drainage problems for agriculture. In contrast the kaolinite Oxisols (with 1:1 silicate clays) are well aerated and well structured, but lack plant nutrients when their natural plant-soil cycle is broken.

There are many examples in the tropics of recent parent materials and areas of high relief that do not show the more typical evidence of advanced chemical weathering that has been described. High rainfall encourages fluvial erosion wherever the plant cover is broken and this contributes to colluvial and alluvial deposits. Other examples of new deposits are volcanic ash parent materials, reasonably widespread in the tropics, particularly in Indonesia and Hawaii. Andosols (which are AC profile Inceptisols) develop on volcanic ash. These deposits, along with parent materials of upland sites, have considerable reserves of weatherable minerals and a higher proportion of 2:1 lattice clays remaining in them than in Oxisols. At these sites, freely draining profiles may become red-yellow podsolics or even podsols. Clay-rich B_t horizons may be found in such less weathered soils, but in time will trend towards the horizon characteristics of Oxisols. Within the humid tropics, it is possible to find a geographical association of soils reflecting different stages of pedogenesis from Inceptisols to Ultisols and to Oxisols.

Grassland soils (Mollisols). In the drier continental interiors of middle and low latitudes, annual and even short period precipitation rarely approaches potential evapotranspiration. Most of the precipitation is lost in actual evapotranspiration and only a relatively small amount finds its way into the groundwater of the soil. High moisture demanding forest vegetation is followed by grassland and progressively by a sporadic distribution of drought resistant plants as aridity increases towards deserts. The freely drained soils of these

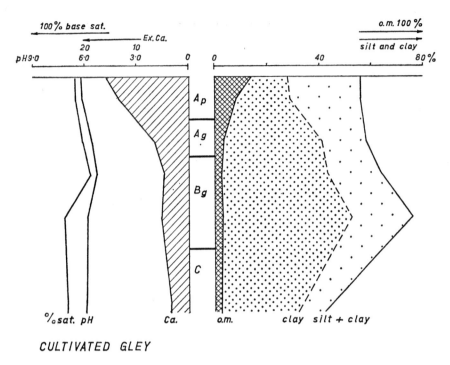

CULTIVATED GLEY

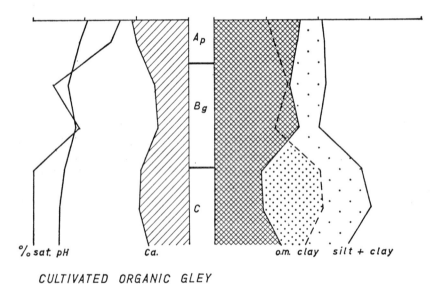

CULTIVATED ORGANIC GLEY

Fig 4:17   Cultivated gleys from the north-east of Scotland. The organic gley (below) would be classed as a Histosol by the high organic content (over 30 per cent) in the solum horizons. The upper diagram represents a soil that might be classed as a Mollisol

environments are affected by leaching, but only on a very small scale and on few occasions. Although the profiles of the Mollisol and Aridisol soil orders are geographically related by their occurrence in sub-humid, semi-arid, and arid environments, their diagnostic characteristics have as many differences as similarities. Mollisols are grassland soils identified by their diagnostic surface horizon which is a deep, dark-coloured humic horizon, saturated with divalent cations (Ca, Mg) and called a mollic epipedon. Because of its humus and its wealth of divalent cations, it has a strong structural development, and the organic matter is decomposed to a low C/N ratio. Mollisols may also have a variety of sub-surface horizons that are argillic (clay-rich), natric (sodium-rich), or cambic (altered but not enriched) so that the soil order includes soils otherwise known as chernozems, prairie soils, reddish prairie soils, solonetz soils, planosols, and even some brown forest soils and rendzinas. Gleys are also included, and indeed humic gleys conform very well with the definition of the order (Fig 4:17), and may occur under anthropogenic grassland over a wide environmental range.

Of all ten orders of the 7th Approximation, the Mollisols probably cover the greatest variety of soil profiles. Their common requirement is an organo-mineral surface horizon, allowing different possibilities for the lower horizons of the A group or a B if present. It allows every degree of drainage to be found so that Mollisols of some type or other are likely to be continuously dominant over extensive areas in grassland environments. Mollisols are the soils of the waterlogged depressions as well as the well drained elevated land. The definition of Mollisols also means that as humic gleys their distribution extends into other bio-climatic environments, particularly where soils have a grass crop. Cultivation of grasses contributes to the development of Mollisols with base-rich, humic surface horizons. Humic gley soils in depressions of cultivation areas in mid-latitude humid environments qualify as Mollisols and are inter-mixed with grey-brown podsolics (Alfisols) or brown earths (Inceptisols). Mollisols occasionally extend beyond the arid limits of continuous grassland cover and, as organic wet site soils are mixed with Aridisols of desert land-scapes. Here, Mollisols have a natric sub-surface horizon into which sodium salts have been carried by capillary movement and water table rise. This horizon is usually clay-rich, with a strong development of columnar structure, the clay having been translocated after a fall in the level of the groundwater table.

The type-example of a Mollisol is the chernozem; it was the first-named and is one of the best known of all soil profiles. The chernozem is the soil of the Russian steppe-lands, the North American Great Plains and prairies, and the pampas of the Argentine. Under natural conditions, it is the typical grassland soil, and even in cultivation, is associated with cereal grass crops. It does not necessarily have a deep A horizon, and although quite darkly stained with humus, this horizon does not contain a large quantity of organic matter. The A horizon is rich in divalent cations, as can be seen from the exchangeable calcium values in Figs 4:18 and 4:19, and has a very high base saturation.

Arid environment soils (Aridisols). Neighbouring Aridisols also include soils with natric horizons (otherwise known as solonchak and solonetz profiles) but with no more than a trace (< 0·5 per cent) of organic matter in their surface horizons. Aridisols are almost completely mineral profiles in arid environments. They are usually dry profiles well above the water table, and there is very little soil solution available for leaching. Deposition of calcium and sodium salts in the profile is related to the depth of moisture percolation from the soil surface together with capillary rise from the water table. This deposition forms the only distinct soil horizon in Aridisols and is found usually within 100 cm of the soil surface. Some Aridisols do have a clay-rich sub-surface horizon, but most are composed of larger size particles and stones. Generally, they lack the basic requirements for agriculture, moisture and nutrient supply, and require irrigation and fertiliser application before crop cultivation is possible. In this aspect, they are a strong contrast to their neighbouring Mollisols.

Soils of arid and semi-arid environments are to be found over nearly one-third of the earth's surface, in Arctic as well as low latitude areas. Temperature regimes cover a wide range, but their common climatic characteristic is a long drought season and otherwise only minimal and infrequent rainfall. The geomorphology of arid lands is also variable, but generally, the lack of a vegetation cover encourages soil instability through removal by wind erosion, sheet wash, and gullying. The relationship between the soil profile and groundwater table is particularly important in arid environments, as the latter is a potential supply of supplementary moisture for both plants and pedogenesis. Because of their

The abundance of rushes (*Juncus communis*) indicates low chemical fertility and gleying to the surface at a site in Co Antrim, Northern Ireland

search for water, many plants develop massive and finely divided root systems so that there is much more organic matter below the soil surface than above it. Moisture carrying dissolved salts can only move a short distance (< 50 cm usually) by capillary attraction upward from a water table that lies within the range of influence of soil surface drying. More commonly calcium sulphate (gypsum) and calcium carbonate are moved downward by percolating water, the more soluble gypsum being carried the further. The depositional horizons are found progressively nearer the soil surface with increasing aridity, and in certain situations form impermeable, cemented pans (see previous chapter). Subsequent truncation of the soil profile by wind and water can expose these cemented pans on the soil surface.

Where groundwater is present—even intermittently—within the solum, concentrations of salts can reach levels toxic to most plants and form distinctive soil horizons. Soils become highly alkaline and saline. Where sodium salts exceed 2 per cent of the mineral matter, a salic horizon is produced which may even be a salt crust on the soil surface under extremely dry conditions and high groundwater table. The soil is called a solonchak. Alkaline soils that show signs of eluviation of clay from the A to B horizons have experienced a drop in the level of the groundwater table. Ultimately, clay-rich horizons may accumulate sufficient exchangeable sodium to make them natric horizons. The continuation of this process of degradation of the upper horizons is called solodisation producing solonetz profiles. These have leached, albic Ae horizons overlying pronounced natric horizons with a columnar structure. The upper part of the soil is acid, but the horizons below are enriched with clay, and sodium salts. Alkaline and saline soils are considered to be halomorphic in profile form, but may be classified either among Mollisols or Aridisols, depending on the character of their surface horizon.

The three remaining orders of the 7th Approximation—Entisols, Vertisols, and Histosols—are each exceptional in some sense. Unlike the other soil orders, they are not connected, even in a loose association, with any single bioclimatic environment, but are genetically controlled by their parent materials or local site conditions. Entisols are mineral soils of recently moved or exposed deposits, and consequently can be found anywhere. Vertisols are

Abandoned agricultural land on the west coast of Ireland which exhibits very clearly raised lazy beds of nineteenth century spade cultivation (see page 213)

(see page 213)

I

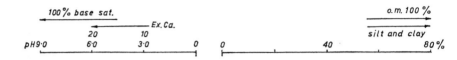

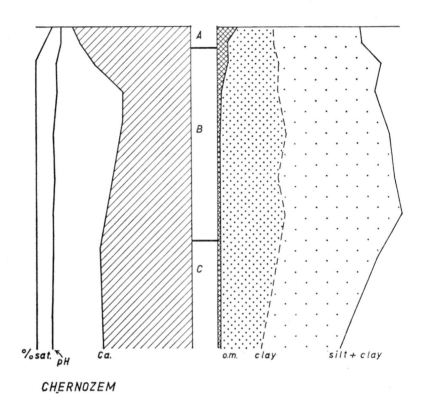

CHERNOZEM

Fig 4:18   Chernozem (Mollisol) developed on calcareous loam till in Barnes County, North Dakota, USA

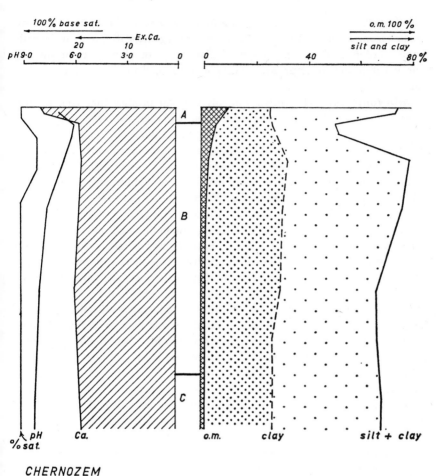

100% base sat.

Ex.Ca.

20   10

pH 9·0   6·0   3·0   0   0   40   80%

100% o.m.

silt and clay

A

B

C

pH
% sat.

Ca.

o.m.   *clay*

silt + clay

CHERNOZEM

Fig 4:19   Chernozem (Mollisol) developed on calcareous loam till in Dickey County, North Dakota, USA

soils of swelling and contracting clays found in a variety of wet and dry season climates from Texas to Australia. Histosols are organic soils. None of the soils in these orders is restricted to a particular region or climatic environment; their distribution is widespread, but divided into small and discontinuous areal units.

Embryonic soils (Entisols). Entisols are soil profiles that lack natural genetic horizons or profile development because of their youthfulness; they are still at an embryonic stage of their development. Because they have not developed soil profile features, their parent material properties may be used for identification. They are found on almost any type of parent material and their solum can vary in depth. Entisols are usually very shallow, stony soils mixed with rock outcrop, and otherwise called lithosols. Such soils are often unstable, ahumic, and patchy in distribution. Regosols (also Entisols) are in some aspects similar; they have deep profiles on unconsolidated mineral materials such as sands, loess, or glacial deposits. Entisols may or may not have surface organic horizons. Usually, lithosols and regosols lack surface organic horizons, but other Entisols depend on them as diagnostic horizons. Cultivated soils comprising mainly a man-made Ap horizon are included in the order if there is no sign of horizonation below, eg, the built-up cultivated soils along parts of the coast in western Ireland. The cultivated horizon may be of any thickness up to the dimensions of *plaggen epipedons*, which have been built-up by centuries of manuring. These man-made cultivation layers are over 50 cm deep and are rich in the nutrients of animal manure (see Chapter 7). As they are only a few hundred years old and as the plaggen epipedon makes up a large proportion of the solum, these plaggen soils are classified in the order of Entisols. In this case and with soils on recent alluvial deposits, the agricultural productivity is high. But Entisols are just as often devoid of agricultural potential, thus showing their characteristic variety in this aspect as well.

Grumusols or Vertisols. Vertisols are one order of soils, but in world distribution they are areally of minor significance (see Fig 4:20). They develop from mineral material containing a high proportion of clay—40 to 70 per cent —most of the clay being a swelling type such as montmorillonite. The soils are otherwise called grumusols—dark coloured clay soils, showing little sign of profile development but having most distinctive physical properties. They are

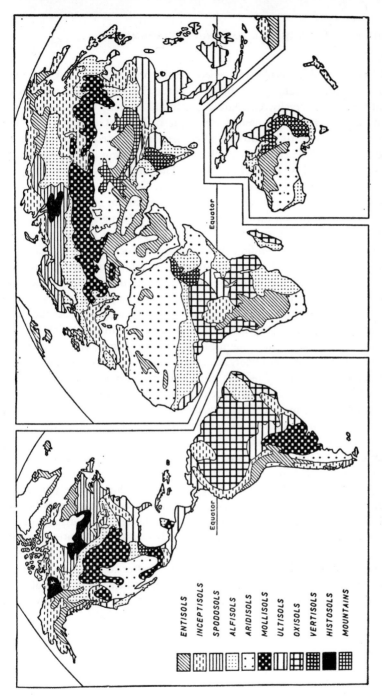

Fig 4:20   Generalised world distribution of the soil orders of the 7th Approximation—adapted from publications of the US Dept of Agriculture, Soil Conservation Service

labelled Vertisols—or inverted soils—because the process of wetting and dry-ing, with consequent swelling and shrinkage of the clay, causes surface particles to fall into dried-out cracks. Grumusols are found in many countries and are known by a variety of local names, eg, regur in India. Generally, they are associated with mid-latitude, sub-humid climates as they require a wet season for the expansion of the clay, and an alternating dry season for clay shrinkage and structural instability; degrees of clay cracking and mixing of mineral par-ticles are related to the length of the dry season. Extremes of expansion and contraction in grumusols, exaggerated by the expansion of clay that has fallen into the cracks, produce an unstable and locally undulating surface, known as gilgai in Australia. This phenomenon limits the potential use of grumusols making them useless for building purposes and reducing their agricultural potential. Despite their physical disadvantages, grumusols are chemically fertile, releasing plant nutrients to crops and not losing them through leaching. Their properties tend to be relatively uniform down the profile except for the amounts of calcium and other soluble salts. Grumusols may be decalcified and acid in reaction, although they are mostly alkaline and nutrient rich. In the Sudan and India, the natural chemical fertility of grumusols makes them attractive for the cultivation of sorghum, maize, millet, and cotton. But here, as in grumusols of eastern Australia and southern United States, these clay soils easily become unworkable with the pressure of farm machinery or draught animals on sticky, plastic clay. When dry, the soils become hard and compacted. Their surface organic matter is low, only 2 to 5 per cent, further detracting from their agricultural potential.

Organic soils. Histosols are profiles with a histic epipedon or an organic surface horizon which is saturated with water for part of the year and overlies other organic horizons. Histosols are organic soils developed largely by accu-mulation of organic debris in a waterlogged site. The site wetness may be due to soil drainage into depressions, raising the groundwater table, or to excessive moisture in the atmosphere as over the uplands of humid climatic environ-ments. Consequently, Histosols may be found as lowland or upland soils. Site wetness reduces or prevents the decay of organic matter so that peat is formed eventually by the build-up of relatively fresh organic litter. The ratio of C/N remains high in these organic deposits. According to the 7th Approximation, histic horizons must have 20 per cent by weight organic matter and over 30 per cent if more than 50 per cent weight of the material is clay. Organic soils always retain a great deal of water because of the exceptional amount of surface area within them and the absorption capacity of the organic matter. The per cent weight organic matter of the dry soil can be as low as 20 per cent even where the soil mass appears to be entirely organic. When mineral particles, especially clay, are mixed through the medium, the per cent weight organic matter requires to be increased to maintain an organic character in the soil. If the per cent organic matter is less than this or if the surface organic horizon is less than 30 cm thick, the soil is more likely to be called a humic gley and classified as an Inceptisol or a Mollisol, depending on the characteristics of the surface organic horizon. The properties and composition of the histic horizon are directly influenced by those of the former plants at the site. As a result Histosols cover the whole range of chemical reaction, but those of lowland depressions are likely to be the most alkaline and base-rich. Because of their location, accessibility, and chemical fertility, lowland Histosols become highly productive agriculturally after drainage. As organic soils dry out, they contract, are oxidised and release nutrient compounds as part of their decay and so are used for intensive cultivation of flowers and vegetables. Their distribution is world-wide although they are more common in humid and cool climates. Their actual distribution is usually divided in small units that cannot be shown on a world distribution map. Organic soils have such unique genesis and properties that they warrant detailed consideration in a later chapter.

Conclusion. This discussion of soil profiles has followed the ten highest categories of the American 7th Approximation soil classification (Fig 4: 21). This has been done for expediency, in order to restrict the total number of soil profiles selected for discussion, as well as in recognition of this widely used soil classification. In the decade since its introduction, the 7th Approximation has been adopted or recognised by several important national soil surveys and has extensively entered soil literature. Of any single soil classification, it has most nearly become accepted universally and it is probable that its importance will be maintained in the next decade. Nevertheless, there are many parts of the 7th Approximation that are either too complicated or too controversial for an introductory text. Even the basic criteria used for sub-division, and hence the actual sub-divisions or lower categories themselves, are controversial because there is no consistency in their selection at the same level within the classification. This is a classification that seems to be of most use to national soil surveys for correlation purposes. The beginner in soil geography is best advised to study and classify soil profiles on the empirical basis of degree and depth of advanced weathering (ie, the depth of solum), state of drainage, and presence or absence of the principal types of horizon. The names of unusual horizons or the names of exceptional soil profiles are not important at an introductory level, and indeed they are even being omitted at an advanced level when pedologists meet at conferences and field meetings—such is the controversy over 'soil labels' at the present time.

Bibliography

BALL, D. F. Brown podzolic soils and their status in Britain, *Journal of Soil Science*, 17 (1966), 148–58.

BLACK, R. F. Permafrost—a review, *Bull. Geol. Soc. Amer.* 65 (1954), 839–56.

BURINGH, P. *Introduction to the study of soils in tropical and subtropical regions.* Centre for Agricultural Publishing and Documentation, Wageningen, 1970.

DAMMAN, A. W. H. Development of some hydromorphic humus podzols and some notes on the classification of podzols in general, *Journal of Soil Science*, 13 (1962), 92–7.

DUCHAUFOUR, P. *Précis de Pédologie*, Masson, Paris, 1960.

FEHRENBACHER, J. B. *et al.* Characteristics of solonetzic soils in Illinois, *Proceedings of the Soil Science Society of America*, 27 (1963), 421–31.

KUBIENA, W. L. *The soils of Europe*, Murby, London, 1953.

KUNZE, G. W. *et al.* Grumusols of the Coast Prairie of Texas, *Proceedings of the Soil Science Society of America*, 27 (1963), 412–21.

MOSS, R. P. (Ed). *The soil resources of tropical Africa*, Cambridge University Press, 1968.

MUIR, A. The podzol and podzolic soils, *Advances in Agronomy*, 13 (1961), 1–56.

MULCAHY, M. J. Laterites and Lateritic soils in South-western Australia, *Journal of Soil Science*, 11 (1960), 206–25.

TAVERNIER, R. and SMITH, G. D. The concept of braunerde in Europe and the United States, *Advances in Agronomy*, 9 (1957), 217–89.

TAMURA, T. *et al.* Properties of brown podzolic soils, *Soil Science*, 90 (1958), 189–97.

TEDROW, J. C. F. Polar Desert soils, *Proceedings of the Soil Science Society of America*, 30 (1966), 381–87.

VAN WAMBEKE, A. Recent developments in the classification of the soils of the tropics, *Soil Science*, 104 (1967), 309–13.

Symposium on tropical soil resources, *Soil Science*, 95 (1963), 219–57.

Sources of data for soil profile diagrams

Figure number		Genetic name	Local name	Source of data
4:4	upper	Brown earth	Darleith Assoc and Series	Soils around Haddington and Eyemouth, HMSO 1967, No 7, p 209
4:4	lower	Brown earth	Leslie Assoc and Series	The Soils round Aberdeen, Inverurie and Fraserburgh, HMSO 1963, No 16, p 263
4:5	upper	Acid brown earth	Ettrick Assoc, Linhope Series	Soils around Haddington and Eyemouth, HMSO 1967, No 22, p 215
4:5	lower	Calcareous brown earth	Fraserburgh Assoc and Series	The Soils round Aberdeen, Inverurie and Fraserburgh, HMSO 1963, No 6, p 258
4:6	upper	Cultivated brown earth	Eckford Assoc and Series	Soils around Haddington and Eyemouth, HMSO 1967, No 15, p 212
4:6	lower	Cultivated brown earth	Ettrick Assoc, Flemington Series	Soils around Haddington and Eyemouth, HMSO 1967, No 24, p 216
4:7	upper	Gley	Netchwood Series	The Soils of the Church Stretton district of Shropshire, HMSO 1966, No 171, p 186
4:7	lower	Gley	Saplings Series	The Soils of the Church Stretton district of Shropshire, HMSO 1966, No 131, p 182

Figure number		Genetic name	Local name	Source of data
4:8	upper	Brown podsolic	New Haven, Conn, USA	Properties of brown podsolic soils, Tamura *et al*
4:8	lower	Brown podsolic	Ettrick Assoc, Linhope Series	(Galloway)—unpublished Soil Survey of Scotland report
4:9	upper	Podsol	Ettrick Assoc, Minchmoor Series	Soils around Haddington and Eyemouth, HMSO 1967, No 71, p 233
4:9	lower	Podsol	Wellheads, Fochabers	Soil Survey of Scotland, Inverness Field Meeting report, 1962
4:10	upper	Peat podsol	Hobkirk Assoc, Faw Series	The Soils round Kelso and Lauder, HMSO 1960, No 22, p 160
4:10	lower	Peat podsol	Reppoch Assoc, Glen Garr Series	The Soils round Kilmarnock, HMSO 1956, No 77, p 203
4:11		Peaty gley	Countesswells Assoc, Drumlasie Series	The Soils around Aberdeen, Inverurie and Fraserburgh, HMSO 1963, No 180, p 319
4:13		Ferruginous tropical soil	Fema Series, Northern Nigeria	*The soils, soil landscapes and geomorphological evolution*
4:14		Ferruginous tropical soil	Du Series, Northern Nigeria	*of a metasedimentary area in northern Nigeria*, R. A.
4:15		Ferruginous tropical soil	Fana Series, Northern Nigeria	Pullan, Univ of Liverpool, 1970
4:16		Ferralitic tropical soil	Ghana	*West African Soils*, P. M. Ahn, Oxford, 1970
4:17	upper	Cultivated gley	Tipperty Assoc, Birness Series	The Soils around Aberdeen, Inverurie and Fraserburgh, HMSO 1963, No 171, p 315
4:17	lower	Cultivated organic gley	Peterhead Assoc and Series	The Soils around Aberdeen, Inverurie and Fraserburgh, HMSO 1963, No 151, p 309
4:18 and		Chernozem	Barnes Co, N Dakota, USA	Chernozems and associated soils of eastern North Dakota, McClelland, J. E. *et al*, Proc. Soil Science Society
4:19		Chernozem	Dickey Co, N Dakota, USA	*al*, Proc. Soil Science Society of America, 23 (1959), 51–6.

CHAPTER FIVE

Soil Classification

THE CONTROVERSY OVER SOIL CLASSIFICATION, WHICH INCLUDES ARGUMENT about definitions and nomenclature, is almost as old as pedology itself. The search for order which is part of any science has been more difficult in this case because of the problem of correlation among soil units, identified by different national surveys in widely scattered parts of the world and labelled in different languages. Even if that initial disadvantage is overcome, it is questioned by some whether soil exists in units that can be classified. Most attempts to classify soils are based on the assumption that the units being classified are discrete and definable, either as profiles or pedons. This premise is frequently challenged now, and most pedologists would agree that soil units for classification are units of convenience created by subjectively chosen breaks in the continuum of soil change. Even if discrete soil units are, in one sense, artificial, they serve an important function as the means of communication and argument among pedologists. Indeed it has been suggested that two levels of soil classification exist, one for non-specialist discussion and general education purposes and the other for professional pedologists concerned with the adjustment and evolution of soil classification to accommodate their research findings.

The following historical outline of attempts to classify soils will deal primarily with widely accepted classifications. It is logical to review soil classifications in chronological order because the character of a classification is a reflection of the state of pedological knowledge of its time. Until quite recently soil classifications were forced to be deductive, their axioms being derived from generalisations made from a limited amount of partially untested data. The classification of parts of a medium that is so variable and so extensive can only by approached with confidence after detailed examination and investigation of the individual parts and properties. This was not possible in the nineteenth century rush to produce classifications concurrently with the earliest pedo-logical research. The Russians, Germans, and Americans produced very simple environmental classifications of soils before 1900, which were based on observed general differences in soils on a continental scale. They were, in fact, classifications of soil-forming environments. The classifications were too general to be of any applied use, and yet too restricted in scope to be reliable outside their continent of origin. The aspirations of the early pedologists to produce a universal classification had not been satisfied, although the prin-ciples of an environmental association for soils had a long lasting influence. Furthermore, it should be remembered that the pre-1900 classifications were not even concerned with the whole profile, but only with the A and C horizons. At that time, the B horizon was regarded simply as a mixture of A and C. If the history of soil classification can be divided into sequential stages, the first phase up to World War I is that of environmental schemes, eg, Cold, Cool-tem-perate, Sub-tropical, and Tropical regions.

Hilgard's classification (1906) divided the North American continent so that a primary sub-division was shown to exist between soils of humid and arid environments. Essentially a distinction was being drawn between the freely draining soils of woodland and non-woodland environments. Ramann (1911) constructed a more elaborate version of the same scheme, and seemed to consider that in the Cool-temperate Zone at least there could be local soil variations from the general rule (see Ramann table). The classification demon-strates very well the almost total ignorance of pedogenesis in the tropics in 1911, and also the assumption that exceptions to the rule of climatic control on pedogenesis must be due to drainage. Russian terminology had been adopted in these classifications which were themselves very similar to the earlier Russian schemes of Dokuchaev and Sibertzev. Both Russians had regarded the most commonly found, freely draining soils of the main climatic zones as *normal* or *zonal* soils; the local exceptions, due to the dominance of some other soil-forming factor, were transitional or *intra-zonal* soils. Soils that had not had an opportunity to develop and therefore could be found in any environment were called *abnormal* or *azonal* soils. This elementary 'zonal soils concept' seems imperfect in the light of current knowledge and is generally regarded as outmoded. It is mainly important for the introduction of Russian profile terms

Ramann's Soil Classification (*1911*)

	HUMID	SEMI-HUMID	SEMI-ARID	ARID
COLD ZONES	ARCTIC —Tesselated soils Flowing earths BOREAL —Tundra soils Peat hillock Tundra REGIONAL—Frost shattered Mountain meadow soils Mountain peat soils			
COOL-TEMPERATE	NORTHERN GREY EARTHS (a) Northern sand-humus soils (b) Podsol (c) Forest bleached earths Local variations 1 Sub-aqueous soils (a) Mineral under water (b) Muds (c) Humus soils 2 Ground water soils (a) Gley (b) Meadow (c) Limonite 3 Receiving site soils (a) Warp soils (b) Marsh soils 4 Saline soils of bleached earths 5 Flowering earths BROWN EARTHS Local variation by parent rock		STEPPE BLACK EARTHS (a) Chernozem (b) Prairie soils (c) Chestnut Brown STEPPE BLEACHED SOILS	
SUB-TROPICAL	YELLOW EARTHS		YELLOW EARTHS RED EARTHS BLACK EARTHS CRUSTING SOILS	CRUSTING DESERT

(*continued over*)

TROPICAL	LATERITE			
	RED EARTHS			
	RED LOAMS			
	RED LOAMS		RED	RED
	TROPICAL BROWN EARTHS	SAVANNA	EARTHS	DESERT
	TROPICAL BLEACHED EARTHS			SOILS

and as the foundation of many other genetic or environmental classifications from the Russian school. Towards the end of the opening phase of soil classification, Glinka (1915) introduced a refinement of earlier Russian schemes, making the primary division between soils developed to maturity mainly by external factors such as climate, and those which were inhibited in their development by internal conditions within the soil, eg, parent material. These groupings were called respectively ektodynamorphic (covering the majority of known soils) and endodynamorphic soils (for the few exceptions). The two groups were further sub-divided according to environmental conditions and the state of drainage of the soil. The classification was considered unsatisfactory even by Glinka's contemporaries because the primary sub-division, being so badly balanced, made little contribution to the scheme. The soil classifications of this first period (1896–1918) did reflect considerable progress in pedological thought and were a notable advance on the previous geological sub-division of soils between residual and transported types (see Chapter 1).

Although modifications of these early classifications persisted for many years, a second stage of soil classification emerged in the late 1920s by which time further research into the physics and chemistry of soils had been assimilated. This was the period (1924–39) of the soil process classifications from the Russians and Americans. In Glinka's later work (Glinka, K. D., 1924), he recognised five major pedogenic processes (lateritic, podsolic, chernozemic, solonetzic, and swampy) on which he based his soil classification. Marbut (1928) established a classification that became the most widely known of the schemes based on soil genesis, in which he made the two-fold primary subdivision between the leached soils (pedalfers) and the non-leached (pedocals) freely drained soils. Marbut's classification was adopted by the United States Soil Survey which greatly increased its application and reputation. In so doing, the intention was that the basic soil unit in field mapping (soil type) should also be the basic unit or lowest category unit in soil classification (see Marbut table). Whether this is possible, even if desirable, has been a point of controversy ever since.

Marbut's Classification (*1928*)

Category		
7	Pedalfers	Pedocals
6	Podsols—temperate humid	Pedocals of temperate zone
	Lateritic soils—tropical humid	Pedocals of tropical zone
5	Tundra	Pedocals grouped by climatic
	Podsols	region within temperate and
	Brown forest soil	tropical zones
	Red soils	
	Yellow soils	
	Prairie soils	
	Laterites	
4	Sub-groups of above or the great soil groups, eg, Chernozem	
	Chestnut brown	
	etc	
3	Drainage and local environment grouping—soil family	
2	Soil series groupings	
1	Soil type = based on texture of surface horizon	
	Soil phase = based on stoniness, slope, or some other exceptional condition of the soil	

This American classification is noteworthy because it incorporated *soil type* and *soil phase*, designed as refinements of soil description of particular use to farmers. This demonstrates very well the applied-to-agriculture character of much American pedological research and publication. The Marbut classification also influenced pedologists on an international level because it was discussed at international soil congresses in 1927, 1932, and 1935. Variations of his classification were published subsequently in a number of other countries, in Britain the example being that of G. W. Robinson (1932), later the first director of the Soil Survey of England and Wales. This was still a simple, genetic classification, based on the division of soil-forming environments, but including recognition of degree of leaching, state of drainage, and type of surface humus.

In Russia, the pedologist Viliams put forward a classification based on the concept of a single pedogenic process (1939) which influenced many subsequent attempts to classify soils. His idea was that all soils were part of a single evolutionary development, beginning with tundra soils, and that all would proceed towards the same ultimate condition given the same time-effective soil-forming conditions. This approach has been severely criticised and largely discredited as being so contrived that it is completely unnatural and unrealistic. It may be regarded as the last of the primarily process classifications and marking the end of the second stage (pre-World War II period) of soil classification.

Controversy on soil classification has revived in the past two decades with the great increase in knowledge about soil processes, expansion of soil survey programmes, publication of several major pedological texts, and the renewal of interest in the principles of taxonomy among pedologists. Much of the argument has been orientated around the pedologists' contribution to taxonomy and whether soils are amenable to classification. With the latter problem, solutions have been found constructively by using both 'natural' and 'artificial' systems. Natural systems are based on subjectively assessed known and unknown properties of the whole soil body, while artificial systems depend on only a selection of three or four measurable soil properties. An inevitable complexity and proliferation of soil classifications in recent years also distinguishes this third and current stage of evolution.

The Austrian pedologist Kubiena (1953 and 1958) attempted to apply the principles of a natural system by ordering soils according to all their characteristics, and not only a few selected properties. His classification grouped soils by the presence and arrangement of horizons in soil profiles, these being regarded as the summation of the whole character of the soil. Kubiena identified five principal groups of soils on the basis of horizon arrangement, namely (A)C, AC, A(B)C, ABC and B/ABC, and used these as sub-divisions of three primary classes based on site conditions (sub-aqueous mineral, flooding and groundwater soils, and terrestrial soils). Similar natural classifications concentrating on horizon arrangement were proposed by Avery in his classification of British soils (1956) and by Duchaufour (1963). Avery first divided soils into well and poorly drained categories, with further sub-division based on surface organic horizon (see Avery table). These natural classifications are in marked contrast to that of Albrecht Thaer who, over a century earlier, distinguished only sand, loam, clay, humus, and lime in soils. The Thaer classification was a forerunner of recent attempts to classify soils by the artificial system of a selection of arbitrarily chosen properties. The resultant groupings of soils do not necessarily bear any relationship to their pedogenic origins, or to their usual field relationships. Artificial classifications appear to take a very limited view of soils, but are more objective and more definitive than most genetic classifications. Types of artificial classification, extending the range of soil properties measured, are becoming more common on an experimental level with the expansion of numerical and computer methods of analysis.

Classification of British soils by B. W. Avery (1956)

A WELL DRAINED TERRESTRIAL SOILS

1	Raw mineral salts	AC profile, including lithosols and regosols
2	Montane humus soils	AC and A(B)C profiles, including rankers
3	Calcareous soils	AC and A(B)C profiles, including rendzinas
4	Leached mull soils	AC and A(B)C profiles, including brown earths, grey-brown podsolics, and brown podsolics
5	Podsolised mor soils	ABC profiles, including podsols

B POORLY DRAINED HYDROMORPHIC SOILS

6	Alluvial (warp) soils	AC and A(B)C profiles, including basic and acid gleys
7	Grey hydromorphic gleys	AC and A(B)C profiles, including mainly basic groundwater gleys
8	Gley-podsolic soils	ABC profiles, including peaty gleyed podsols
9	Peaty alkaline soils	AC profiles, including fen gleys
10	Peat bog	acid moss peat, including blanket peat and raised bog

Numerical taxonomy of soil is defined as the numerical evaluation of property similarities among soil units, and the subsequent ordering of these units into groups on the basis of their affinities. The fundamental principles were first outlined by Adanson (1763) in his effort to find a logical basis for 'natural

K

groups' among molluscs and plants—for example, (a) groups are based on information about as many properties, features, or characteristics as possible; (b) every characteristic is given equal weight in constructing 'natural' groups; (c) overall similarity is a function of the proportion of the characteristics in common; (d) affinity or grouping is regarded as independent of the postulated genesis. The computer has enabled the soils investigator to apply the numerous characteristics required by Adanson, and between forty and sixty are desirable for the method to be reliable with soils. Classification is based on a matrix of resemblances, and it consists of various techniques designed to disclose and summarise the structure of a matrix. The greatest similarity exists among individuals grouped together in the lowest categories, and the higher rank taxa are based on progressively lower levels of affinity (Bidwell and Hole, 1964). The method creates a hierarchical system, based on quantitative estimates of the similarities within groups of soils; it makes the assumption that the taxonomic value of every characteristic is equal. This may be justified in biology, but in pedology the genesis of soils is so far inadequately known to say if this premise is valid. Numerical classification is appealing in that it is part of the quantitative trend in the natural sciences, but its development requires more understanding of the relationships among soil properties, particularly whether they can be ascribed equal weighting, and of the relationship between soil properties and soil profiles in their spatial variation.

Currently, the most controversial and yet the most nearly successful as a universally adopted soil classification is the US Department of Agriculture Soil Survey's 7th Approximation (1960). It is so called because it was the seventh attempt of its authors in their search for the ideal classification. It has been received controversially because of its nomenclature, and because its categories are based on a specific definition of diagnostic soil properties. Its language is new and is derived from a number of sources, mainly from Latin, to encourage universal acceptance. It uses rather forbidding new soil terms, and even now, only a few pedologists would be able to use more than the principal order names with confidence. These order names are composed of formative elements which refer to characteristic properties and are compounded with additional syllables at each successive sub-division level. For example, at the 'great soil group' level of soil profile names, a 'plintumbrult' is a member of the Ultisols with an organic surface horizon and diagnostic plinthite below, and a 'fraglossudalf' is an Alfisol with a tongued albic horizon and fragipan.

Formative elements in names of soil orders

Name of order	Formative element in name of order	Derivation of formative element	Summary characteristics
Entisol	ent	Nonsense syllable	recent soils
Vertisol	ert	L *verto*, turn	inverted soils
Inceptisol	ept	L *inceptum*, beginning	inception—young soils
Aridisol	id	L *aridus*, dry	arid soils
Mollisol	oll	L *mollis*, soft	organo-calcimorphic soils
Spodosol	od	Gk *spodos*, wood ash	podsols
Alfisol	alf	Nonsense syllable	leached basic soils
Ultisol	ult	L *ultimus*, last	deeply weathered, red podsols
Oxisol	ox	F *oxide*, oxide	oxides of iron and aluminium (ferrallitic)
Histosol	ist	G *histos*, tissue	organic soils

Many of the diagnostic properties used in this classification are so narrowly defined that laboratory analysis is necessary before a soil class can be established. The precision and relative absence of overlapping ranges of property values has provoked strong criticism from some pedologists but the classification is useful in arranging soils for which such data is available. The 7th Approximation is still based on pedogenesis, the criteria of categories being soil properties indicative of or produced by particular pedogenic processes. However, in this case the primary soil orders are not associated with climatic or geographic environments, but are based on internal characteristics of the diagnostic horizon. This has been regarded as one of the merits and advances of the 7th Approximation, despite the fact that departure from the environmental approach has also meant the omission of gleying as a separate order. Gleys can be found in most of the primary orders so that in these orders more than one pedogenic process is represented. This apparent anomaly demonstrates very well that this classification is structured around narrow property and horizon definitions, and relegates soil-forming processes to a subsidiary role. Compared with earlier genetic classifications, the approach is unconventional and results in some unexpected associations or groupings of soils. Unless great care is taken in measuring properties and identifying horizons, it is likely that a soil may be placed in the wrong primary order. Leached soils and even podsols are spread over more than one order because greater emphasis is given to soil property values and horizon limits than to pedogenesis. It has been questioned by some whether soils may be organised in such a rigid manner, and although the system appears to be more objective than its predecessors, it requires considerable pedological information to be workable.

In any kind of classification, there is a great temptation to follow the classical model of a nested hierarchy of categories and this has been done in most soil classifications, including the 7th Approximation. Correctly, such classifications should adopt the same criteria for the sub-division of classes at any one category level. However, the 7th Approximation uses the modification traditionally allowed for 'natural classifications' by introducing any distinguishing characteristics found suitable as a criteria for sub-division. These have been found by the subjective decision of the soil taxonomists as the criteria most likely to reveal natural differences among soils, and are criteria delimited by highly specific ranges of values. This classification has many pitfalls for the novice, and is being used principally by soil survey organisations that have accumulated soil data in a form usable in this system. The 7th Approximation is now widely used by national soil surveys, even if only in the form of a translation of their own classifications, and has been used by organisations like FAO for the publication of world soil maps. This must be recognised as a measure of international acceptance and use.

Probably the most notable feature of the 7th Approximation is the attention given to soil profile morphology and to soil property evaluation of diagnostic horizons. In doing so, it has influenced a current trend of adopting horizon characteristics and horizon arrangement as criteria for the classification of soil profiles, in place of concepts about soil genesis. A recent example is the classification of E. A. FitzPatrick (1967) in which soil profiles are labelled with a formula composed of horizon letters, each with a subscript number referring to horizon thickness. Soils are grouped into classes on the basis of similarity in formula, but unlike the 7th Approximation and other natural classifications, FitzPatrick departs from the tradition of erecting a hierarchical system. His approach seems more realistic in recognising that the nature of soils cannot be organised into hierarchies of genealogically related members. Soils are grouped in his scheme into independent sub-classes and classes if they have two or three prominent horizons in common. This appears to be a simple and workable system in which the operator is mainly concerned with recording field characteristics by letters and numbers. Certainly the challenges of decision making presented by any hierarchical system have been removed, but the operator is still required to equip himself with a comprehensive dictionary of pedological terms to find the appropriate horizon symbols!

The problem of nomenclature is a reflection of most current soil classifications, which in turn are an expression of the advancement of pedological knowledge. The more that is known about the complexity of the three-dimensional continuum of soil, the more it becomes obvious that classification has to depend on the character of pedons even if their areal boundaries are arbitrarily chosen. It is recognised that soil classification, in dealing with the gradual and continuous variation of a continuum, is not concerned with discrete units; they rarely exist in soil. Nevertheless it is necessary to classify the most commonly occurring soil units, arbitrarily delimited as they may be, as a means of communication, education, and implementation of research findings. There is much to be said in favour of using the new terms of the 7th Approximation, however perplexing for the beginner, in that they do encourage more flexibility than the traditional A, B, C horizon letters that are tied too rigidly to traditional concepts of pedogenesis. Even greater flexibility is given by schemes such as those of FitzPatrick (1967) and Northcote (1960) which avoid using a complex hierarchical system of categories.

The Northcote soil classification, which was used in the *Atlas of Australian Soils* 1962, is based on observable properties of soil profiles and not on any theory of pedogenesis. The soil properties used are texture, colour, carbonate content, acidity, and cementation. A hierarchy of categories exists only to the extent that soils are grouped initially by their texture range through the profile. There are four primary divisions; U is for profiles of uniform texture, G for profiles having a gradational change in texture, D for profiles with a contrasting (duplex) change in texture, and O for organic profiles. Within these four groups, each soil profile is given a formula of letters and numbers (eg, UC 4.31) which represents a particular combination of surface and sub-surface horizons, each with a specified range of soil property values. Once again, the classification can be used only with the help of a long explanatory key, but it attempts to be objective and relatively simple in the selection of soil properties used as distinguishing criteria.

For the student of geography and others interested in an introduction to pedology, one of the less sophisticated groupings of soil profiles on the basis of horizon combinations is still the best means of learning about the spatial variation of soils and the problems of their classification. The working classification used by the national soil survey of one's own country should be the guide for every student of pedology. The 'national philosophy' on classification and terminology has now evolved in response to soil formation conditions in the country concerned, and should be adopted in the educational training of that country.

Bibliography

ADANSON, M. *Familles des Plants*, Vincent, Paris, 1763.

AVERY, B. W. A classification of British soils, *6th International Congress of Soil Science*, E (1956), 279–85.

BASINSKI, J. J. The Russian approach to soil classification and its recent development, *Journal of Soil Science*, 10, no 1 (1959), 14–26.

BIDWELL, O. W. and HOLE, F. D. Numerical taxonomy and soil classification, *Soil Science*, 97 (1964), 58–62.

CLINE, M. G. Logic of the new system of soil classification, *Soil Science*, 96 (1963), 17–22.

DUCHAUFOUR, P. Soil classification: A comparison of the American and French systems, *Journal of Soil Science*, 14 (1963), 149–55.

FITZPATRICK, E. A. Soil nomenclature and classification, *Geoderma*, 1 (1967), 91–105.

GLINKA, K. D. *Pedology*, St. Petersburg, 1915.

GLINKA, K. D. Différents types d'après lesquels se forment les sols et la classification de ces derniers, *Comité Int. Pédologie*, IV, Commis No 20, 1924.

HILGARD, E. W. *Soils*, Macmillan, New York, 1906.

JONES, T. A. Soil Classification—a destructive criticism, *Journal of Soil Science*, 10 (1959), 196–200.

KNOX, E. G. Soil individuals and soil classification, *Proceedings of Soil Science Society of America*, 29 (1965), 79–84.

KUBIENA, W. L. The classification of soils, *Journal of Soil Science*, 9 (1958), 9–19.

KUBIENA, W. L. *The soils of Europe*, Murby, London, 1953.

LEEPER, G. W. The classification of soils, *Journal of Soil Science*, 7 (1956), 59–64.

MANIL, G. General considerations on the problem of soil classification, *Journal of Soil Science*, 10 (1959), 5–13.

MARBUT, C. F. A scheme for soil classification, *1st International Congress of Soil Science*, 4 (1928), 1–31.

MUIR, J. W. The general principles of classification with reference to soils, *Journal of Soil Science*, 13 (1962), 22–30.

NORTHCOTE, K. H. *A factual key for the recognition of Australian soils*, Division of Soils, CSIRO, 1960.

RAMANN, E. *Bodenkunde*, Berlin, 1911.

ROBINSON, G. W. *Soils, their origin, constitution and classification*, Murby, London, 1932.

SMITH, G. D. Objectives and basic assumptions of the new soil classification system, *Soil Science*, 96 (1963), 6–16.

SOIL SURVEY STAFF, *Soil classification—a comprehensive system*, 7th Approximation, US Department of Agriculture, Washington, 1960 and 1967.

VILIAMS, V. R. *Pedology*, Selkhozgiz, Moscow, 1939.

WEBSTER, R. Fundamental objections to the 7th Approximation, *Journal of Soil Science*, 19 (1968), 354–65.

CHAPTER SIX

Soil as an Organic Medium

Introduction

ORGANIC MATTER MAKES A SOIL COME ALIVE; ITS IMPORTANCE CANNOT BE overstated. It includes both the food supply for soil organisms and the community of organisms itself. Soil organisms help to convert organic matter into nutrient compounds which, in turn, help to support plant life. In other ways organic matter may further improve soil as a growing medium for plants by modifying soil structure, temperature, and water-holding capacity in a desirable way. Organic matter enters soil as soon as the first plant organisms—usually primitive plants like bacteria or algae—become established. Higher forms of plant life follow later. Decomposition of organic litter and incorporation of the decay products into the soil system start when the first plants die. All the time decomposition is taking place, fresh organic litter is being added to the soil. The balance between the two is reflected in the amount and state of soil organic matter, and indeed in the morphology of the soil profile itself.

'Soil as an organic medium' is not used here to imply consideration only of soils containing a high proportion of organic matter, but as a widely embracing theme to include all ways in which organic matter is present and may affect the soil system. These include the following:

a accumulation and decay of organic litter
b constituents of soil organic matter
c the community of soil organisms: their ecology and the areas of maximum activity in soil
d organic soils—or soil as an almost completely organic medium
e surface organic horizons
f mineralisation of organic matter or nutrient cycles involving soil organic matter

g the effect of organic solids and solutions on soil profile development and on soil properties—discussed mainly in other chapters.

Organic matter in the soil may profoundly affect its development, but this influence must be differentiated from that of vegetation as a soil-forming factor. The former is an integral part of the soil and modifies it from within. Vegetation is an external factor, interrelated with other soil-forming factors, and provides organic litter to the soil as only one of the ways in which it may affect soil formation. For example, vegetation has another role in influencing the water balance between the soil and the atmosphere.

Soil may be regarded as an organic medium by being a habitat for free-living organisms. Even apparently mineral soils are habitats for a multitude of different species and populations of micro- and macro-organisms. In most soils their activity is most intense in a surface horizon of organic matter. Where organic matter is so thick that it comprises a large proportion of the total soil, it must be classified as a separate and distinctive category of soils. Soil micro-biologists or ecologists do not worry about this distinction, but pedologists, such as the US Soil Survey Staff, have produced definitions for organic horizons and organic soils. An organic horizon must contain at least 20 per cent organic matter by weight (or 30 per cent if the mineral fraction is half clay) and be less than 30 cm (12 in) thick. An organic soil is composed of an accumulation of decaying organic matter, in the same weight proportion as the horizon, greater than 30 cm in thickness. Normally an organic soil is greater than 1 m in thickness and provides the rooting medium for surface vegetation. These are the definitions of the American 7th Approximation which adopts the terms 'histic horizon' and 'histosols' for these pedological units.

Decay of organic litter. Decay of organic litter involves several processes, both physicochemical and biological, which ultimately change litter into solid mineral matter, carbon dioxide gas, moisture, and amorphous organic matter known as *humus*. The term humus is used most frequently for this dark and sticky transitional product of organic decay but also as a general term for all surface and sub-surface organic horizons. It is used, therefore, to describe both the state of organic matter as well as certain organic formations in soil. Either way, humus itself contains a number of different organic compounds.

Organic litter is changed into humus and other materials both by the direct activity of soil organisms as well as by chemical reactions with which organisms are concerned only indirectly or not at all. Direct oxidation of organic litter is occasionally possible in desert situations, but far more commonly chemical reactions are conducted by enzymes excreted by soil organisms. These enzyme substances, present in the immediate vicinity of their parent organism, are able independently to hydrolyse organic matter. The compounds produced by hydrolysis may later be absorbed by soil organisms and further changes of the organic compound, also conducted by enzymes, will take place during digestion by organisms. Such biochemical reactions are links in a complex chain of changes from the original organic litter to the ultimate end-products of decomposition. Raw organic litter enters the soil with a complicated chemical structure of linked atoms and molecules. Change into simple chemical compounds necessitates a number of stages of degradation, losing and changing the arrangement of molecules. It is important to recognise that organic decomposition has to be a multiple-stage process, because of the chemical complexity of the original litter and relative simplicity of the end-products like carbon dioxide, ammonia, and mineral salts. The process of change is sometimes called 'polymerisation' because it involves the formation of polymers, new organic compounds made from multiples of molecules. Single molecules (monomers) combine to make up polymers which have the same proportions of constituent atoms in the new compound as in the old.

The rate and nature of organic decomposition depends partly on the constituents of the organic litter, as some of these are more easily altered than others. Easily attacked by a wide variety of soil micro-organisms are substances like protein, sugars, and pectins which are all water-soluble, as well as several other simple carbohydrate or starch compounds. The second group includes more complex carbohydrates like celluloses and hemi-celluloses. The last and most resistant group includes compounds like waxes, resins, and lignin which are found as protective tissue on the outer skins of leaves, etc. If all other limiting factors are constant the rate of organic decay among comparative sites will be controlled by the proportions present of these three groups of constituent compounds. Proteins are rich in nitrogen; and celluloses, lignin, and other compounds of the second and third groups contain particularly high proportions of carbon, and therefore a second yardstick by which the rate of decay can be measured is the ratio of carbon to nitrogen in the fresh litter. A division of leaf litter may be made as follows:

C/N ratio of litter

1 Grasses, herbaceous plants, and tree species
   like alder and ash   10–20
2 Broadleaf deciduous tree species like horn-
   beam, elm, lime, and oak   20–50
3 Broadleaf deciduous tree species like birch,
   beech, maple, and poplar   50–60
4 Most needle-leaf conifer species and heath
   plants as well as any woody tissues   50–110

As there is an increase in the amount of carbon to be oxidised into carbon dioxide gas, the litter of each successive group requires approximately an extra year for complete decomposition at comparable sites, and the leaf litter of larch and all woody tissues may require five years or more in mid-latitude humid environments. The degree of degradation may be measured by the new compounds formed, and its completion by a C/N ratio of about 10–12, expected in well-decomposed soil organic horizons.

The decay of organic litter can be divided into various forms of attack by soil organisms. In some cases, leaf tissue is attacked while still on the plant because some leaf surfaces excrete sugars which serve as the initial food for micro-organisms like bacteria and fungi. Fungi are the micro-organisms usually responsible for the primary attack on fresh litter, making the internal solutions, sugars, and starches the first to disappear. The casing of cell wall material survives for subsequent physical breakdown and removal by soil fauna, followed by decomposition by enzymes secreted by micro-organisms. The functioning of the two groups interrelate in a complex system, the enzyme attack sometimes actually taking place inside the soil animal or in its discarded faeces.

During decay, some of the organic carbon is converted by soil organisms into carbon dioxide which is released during their respiration. Moisture and some other gases (such as ammonia, NH_3) are also released by their metabolism. Other soil organisms are able to convert some of these gases by oxidation or reduction into other mineral compounds. The rest of the organic matter survives in an altered and chemically rearranged form as humus. This can be broken into organic fractions such as humin, humic acid, hymato-melanic acid, and fulvic acid, the last three each soluble in a different solvent. Humin is insoluble in any solvent and consists of highly resistant carbonaceous material. Humic acid is alkali soluble, for example, in sodium hydroxide, while hymato-melanic acid is soluble in alcohol and fulvic acid in another acid. Fulvic acid is the most effective organic solution for the mobilisation and transportation of acid-soluble soil compounds.

Humus, with its constituent compounds and solutions, can remain in the soil for an extremely long time without forming any spectacular accumulation. From field examples in Canada, Sweden and Britain, carbon-14 dating methods have been used to measure the life of humic acids in the B horizon of podsols at between 400 and 2,800 years, with a 'mean residence' of about 1,000 years (Burges and Raw, 1967). This is to be expected from what is only a small residual fraction of the original organic matter, and a potentially mobile product. Compared with the source litter, the quantity of humus left in soil is minimal; it is mobile because it is composed largely of organic solutions and colloids. Humic acid is the dominant constituent in quantitative terms, and usually includes a variety of humic compounds. Many of these, as well as other constituents of humus, can be regarded as phenols or phenolic substances, ie, any organic compound that is composed of a hydroxyl (OH) molecule attached to a benzene ring structure. Phenols are produced by the rearrangement or polymerisation of molecules during organic decay. Some of these organic phenols can function as '*chelates*' and conduct the process of *chelation*. This happens when an organic solution forms a complex with a metallic ion such as iron, from which it cannot dissociate. The metal is kept in solution and can be transported around the soil body in this combination. It may even be absorbed by plants in this form. Chelation makes possible the translocation through the soil profile of organic compounds containing iron as iron humate, as well as complexes of aluminium and magnesium. Buried or sub-surface humic horizons develop by this means or simply by the physical movement down profile of organic solutions. Such humus enrichment of B horizons in podsols is a slow process, but one that produces distinctive morphological characteristics.

The soil community. The size of the community of soil organisms is almost beyond our comprehension; its ecological importance is appreciated but not fully understood. It is obvious that soil organisms, presented with the formidable challenge of the input of organic litter, are successful each year in their decomposition of most of it. Accumulation of litter on the soil surface for more than four or five years is the exception rather than the rule, and is explained by the local habitat being in some way unfavourable to soil organism activity.

The scale of annual decay of organic litter may be appreciated by starting with the annual production of living vegetable matter. This is familiar to us all and is seen mainly in the form of a renewal or increase in plant leaves, the greatest part of the annual production being in the leaf canopy. Production of vegetable matter also occurs in root systems and woody parts above the ground, but taking all plant forms into account, at least two-thirds of the annual increase is in the leaves. Of course, dead organic litter has lost most of the moisture contained in the living plant, but despite that, the dry matter weight of litter fall is about 5 tons per acre per year from woodland in middle latitude humid environments. It may vary from half as much to twice as much according to vegetation type within the same climatic region, and on a world scale from a small fraction of 5 tons in desert or tundra environments to over twice as much in tropical rain forest. The amounts are large and would be an embarrassment to any refuse disposal unit designed by man! Fortunately, nature takes care of the situation by providing an army of small organisms to conduct the decomposition in the soil. It is possible to find 1 ton per acre of bacteria—only one group of soil organism although admittedly the most populous—and it has been estimated that the weight of the whole community of soil organisms is twenty times that of the human population on the earth.

It is clear that the human population could not survive without this living refuse disposal unit of soil organisms. Its ecological function is second only to that of green plants in conducting the energy conversion or food-making process of photosynthesis. Indeed, it is generally acclaimed that photosynthesis and organic decay are the two most important processes in nature. Of course, man has now devised supplementary supplies of the mineral elements (mainly nitrogen, phosphorus, and sulphur) required by cultivated plants, but the removal of organic litter and natural cycling of certain mineral nutrients is vital to all other plants. Most important of all, man has not invented any other way of maintaining the carbon dioxide stock in the atmosphere apart from his temporary bonanza from an escalating consumption of fossil fuel. The release of carbon dioxide from this source is only an extension of the natural process of organic decomposition.

There are so many different species of soil organism—at any one soil site there may be over 2,000 species and the total number of identified species of soil organism is about 4,000—that the combined community has a very wide ecological tolerance and performs a variety of functions. Soil organisms comprise both plant and animal species; the smallest organisms are micro-flora like bacteria, fungi, and algae, and slightly larger are the species of meso- and macro-fauna. All are simply constructed organisms; they are ancient and primitive on the evolutionary scale. Except for their moisture requirement for life and reproduction, soil organisms make few special demands on their habitat. Because of these characteristics, members of the soil community have a great deal in common, and in many cases, may replace each other functionally. In the ecosystem of the soil there are some, but comparatively few, ecological niches that can be filled by only one or a restricted group of species. The majority share a wide and common distribution. Similar species composition can be found in the soil fauna among similar soil sites in the Arctic tundra, British woodlands, and tropical rain-forest. A much greater difference may be found in species composition between well drained mineral soils and adjacent peat bog. This illustrates that the spatial variation in species composition of the soil community is more likely to be controlled by soil conditions, particularly by the proportions of soil air and moisture in the pore space and by chemical status, and less by differences in vegetation and regional climate. The metabolism of soil organisms, ie, the rate at which their body processes and hence organic litter decomposition takes place, does respond to temperature, and thus climate exerts control over the spatial variation of that function. The rate of litter decomposition is between two and four times faster in tropical rain-forest than in mid-latitude forest. However, the same species composition and even comparable numbers of soil organisms may be found in both.

Despite the apparent uniformity of species composition among sites at both a continental and plant community level of sampling, there is a marked distribution pattern of soil organisms at any one site. There are three main areas of organism activity naturally related to the sources of organic litter or substrate. These are:

1 Within leaf litter accumulating on the surface of the mineral soil.
2 Within and immediately surrounding the roots—the *rhizosphere*.
3 On the surface of living aerial parts of plants, particularly on the leaves —the *phyllosphere*.

The first of these is the area of greatest soil organism numbers and activity. Many biologists have described a vertical zonation of organisms, of soil fauna in particular, within the surface litter. Those micro-flora that contain chlorophyll and make their own food by photosynthesis, such as the blue-green algae, are found in the full-light conditions of the surface of the litter or mineral soil. Soil faunal species often have structural modifications best suited to the available space and lighting of a particular layer of the surface litter, although habitat segregation is not rigid. In the second and third areas of organism activity, the plant attracts micro-organisms to the surfaces of its roots and leaves by the release of organic solutions. These so-called 'exudate' solutions contain sugars and amino acids. In the case of the leaves, the exudate is easily and usually washed off, so contributing to the organic solutions in the surface litter. Only in the tropical rain-forest does bacterial activity become significant—in decay and nitrogen-making processes—on the surface of tree-canopy leaves. However, at all sites, plant roots have a rhizosphere, created by their excreted organic solutions and maintained by vast numbers of organisms. Micro-organisms are between 50 and 200 times more numerous in the rhizosphere than in other areas of the mineral soil. Some of them actually enter the root system to establish mutually advantageous (symbiotic) relationships or a parasitic relationship in the host plant. Numbers of soil organisms per unit volume reach a peak in the rhizosphere and in the soil surface litter, there being a decreasing gradient of numbers away from each of these areas.

The soil community is composed of several thousand distinct species which belong to a number of taxonomic divisions of the plant and animal kingdom (see Table 6:1). The micro-organisms of the soil are mainly plant species, but they do include the protozoa from the animal kingdom. The micro-flora found in the soil are in one of the two sub-kingdoms of plants, the Thallophytes, which are single-cell plants with little body or surface differentiation. They live in a fluid medium, and are capable of fast rates of reproduction. The larger soil fauna function as an important control on the numbers of microflora present in the soil. They are so small that individuals are invisible to the human eye, and can only be studied with a microscope. Bacteria, for example, are comparable in size to a clay particle. Fungi and algae form colonies which can be seen and are similar in overall shape to higher forms of plants.

Bacteria are the smallest and always the most numerous of soil organisms. In the smallest measurable weight or volume of soil, there are millions, if not billions, of bacteria present. In a teaspoonful of soil, the population of bacteria may be twice the total human population of the earth. However, they weigh only about 0·2 per cent of the weight of any soil sample—a similar proportion to that of fungi. Soil is not regarded as the best habitat for bacteria and only a fraction of them are able to make use of it. Soil bacteria include so many species that collectively they are tolerant of a wide range of ecological conditions. All require moisture and most require a direct source of oxygen from surrounding air. The majority of soil bacteria prefer an intermediate to alkaline chemical status, but as a group they are found from pH 4·0 to 10·0. Their optimum temperature range (shared by most soil organisms) is from 25° to 35° C, but bacteria have been found active at 4° C in Arctic soils and 10° C is a usual lower threshold temperature for bacterial activity. Most bacteria are heterotrophic, feeding directly on organic litter or that which has been predigested by soil fauna. This is a highly important function as it is the basis of organic decomposition and the oxidation of carbon. Bacteria require nitrogen for this process, and if it is not available in sufficient quantity in the litter, they draw on reserves of nitrogen in the soil. To compensate for this temporary loss of soil nitrogen, it is fortunate that some bacteria help to provide soil nitrogen as part of their own food-making process. These are autotrophic bacteria that independently make their carbohydrate food by using carbon dioxide, and not by feeding on organic litter. The by-product, which is the release of more oxygen than carbon consumed by the autotrophs, allows the oxidation of nitrogen, phosphorus, and sulphur compounds into forms usable by plants. It is interesting that these bacteria which do not take part directly in organic decomposition should play such a notable role in the mineralisation of organic compounds (see later section).

Table 6:1

Soil organisms (divisions of micro-flora, micro- and macro-fauna)	Total number of species in soil	Population Number of organisms/m²	Number of organisms/g	Probable biomass proportions
Micro-flora				
BACTERIA	250		$1-10 \times 10^9$ ($1-3 \times 10^9$ common)	
FUNGI	700		Similar weight to bacteria but hyphae makes number estimates difficult— *c* 500,000 individuals	
ACTINOMYCETES	50		10–15 million	
ALGAE	50 genera *c* 750 species		5,000–3 million (100,000–200,000 common)	All micro-flora 1,800
Micro-fauna				
PROTOZOA	250–300	20,000– 200 million	*c* 100,000	35
Meso-fauna				
NEMATODA (eelworms)	1,000	1–30 million (5–10 million common)		5
Macro-fauna				
ARTHROPODA	300–400	20,000–180,000 (up to 2 million possible)		1

(continued over)

L

Soil organisms (Divisions of micro-flora, micro- and macro-fauna)	Total number of species in soil	Population Number of organisms/m²	Number of organisms/g	Probable biomass proportion.
OLIGOCHAETA				
(a) Enchytraeidae (small worms 5–10 mm)	232	10,000–300,000		1
(b) Lumbricidae (earthworms)	220	50–500		350
MOLLUSCA	50	150–200		70
TOTAL SPECIES NUMBER	Minimum 2,000 — maximum 4,000 +			Total 2,262

Fungi are often complementary to bacteria in range of habitat. More fungi tolerate acid conditions than bacteria, and they are often the dominant micro-organism of extremely acid soils. Fungi often initiate the decomposition attack on woody and other carbonaceous tissues. They may be less numerous than bacteria per unit volume of soil, but because they develop long filaments (hyphae) about 2μ in diameter, their weight and volume in soil is similar to that of bacteria. The complex growth of hyphae (called a mycelium) sometimes acts as a trapping net to catch other organisms mobile in the soil. Larger organisms—soil fauna like protozoa and nematode worms—are trapped in this way and so become the food supply of the much smaller fungi. As nematodes multiply rapidly and have relatively few ecological advantages, fungi are being constructive in controlling their number. In addition to their most useful function as saprophytes on woody material, fungi are sometimes parasitic on other living organisms and also enter symbiotic relationships with organisms like algae.

Actinomycetes develop filaments and have a growth form like fungi. However, they are more often grouped with bacteria and tend to have similar environmental preferences. They cannot tolerate acid conditions. Actinomycetes can secrete antibiotic solutions which can benefit themselves by controlling the multiplication of bacteria where the two groups are in competition.

Algae are found at or near the soil surface. Most require light because they have chlorophyll and make their food by photosynthesis. Many other species of algae are not found in the soil, but are inhabitants of aquatic sites. Even in soil, they prefer wet sites. Soil algae are mostly from the green, blue-green and yellow-green groups. They are very useful organisms, especially the blue-green algae, which can fix nitrogen directly from the atmosphere. As they can spring into activity on the soil surface whenever enough moisture is supplied, they are a temporary but important source of organic matter in arid soils, as well as being a source of nitrogen wherever they occur.

Lichens can be seen as crust-like colonies—orange, brown, and black—which are the result of a symbiotic relationship between soil fungi and algae. On freshly exposed mineral soil, they are often pioneer plants which provide organic matter for succeeding higher forms of plant life.

Soil fauna are all invertebrates, and make up 15 to 20 per cent by weight of the soil community. Their ecological value is proportionately much greater as they perform the useful functions of predigesting and spreading organic litter for the benefit of smaller and less mobile organisms, as well as mixing humus with mineral soil.

Protozoa are the smallest of soil animals and are often associated with the micro-flora in a close predator-prey relationship. Many species prey exclusively on bacteria and their population size fluctuates according to the variation in that food supply. Other protozoa feed on fungi, algae, and directly on organic litter. There are many respects in which they are markedly different from the micro-flora. They are at least ten times greater in size, and graze a much larger habitat because of increased size and mobility. Protozoa exist in several life-forms, but generally are able to propel themselves freely through the soil by the means of whip-like organs. They are dependent on moisture for this freedom of movement, but can survive periods of drought in a dormant stage. Protozoa have a wide acidity tolerance and some are found in very acid soils where their food supply has to be fungi. In extremely acid conditions of sphagnum bog or peaty 'mor' litter, some protozoa become ecologically more important than fungi as decay organisms. While they are mainly useful as a control on bacterial populations, they themselves are the food supply of nematodes.

Nematoda or nematode eelworms are a much discussed group of soil animals (probably because they can be present in enormous numbers), are of controversial ecological significance and are just big enough to be visible to the human eye. They are worm-shaped organisms with a tough surface, 0·5–1·5 mm in length which makes them at least ten times as big as protozoa. They are the smallest soil organisms that can easily be extracted from soil and collected in the free living state. Nematodes do not take part in the direct decomposition of organic litter, but instead live on liquid food—protoplasm—drawn out from living plant cells and bacteria. Nematodes are often parasitic in living plants, for example, as the potato eelworm pest, and have a great capacity to survive temporary adversity in their habitat. Many species are regarded as pests both in the soil community and the ecosystem at large.

Arthropoda or arthropods include a wide range of soil animals such as centipedes, millipedes, insects, beetles, termites, woodlice, and springtails. They share the common characteristic of having jointed legs. Many species of arthropod are not much bigger than nematodes, but the largest can be about ten times the size. Arthropods are so varied in life-form and habitat that there are species for almost every type of organic litter. The springtails (Collembola), capable of springing relatively great distances, become dominant macro-fauna in acid peat in the absence of millipedes and earthworms. Mites (Acarina) are also common in acid organic litter. Some of the arthropods are vegetarian and serve the function of predigesting organic litter before it is attacked by bacteria and fungi. Others, like centipedes, are carnivorous on smaller soil fauna, even on other arthropods.

Oligochaeta are sub-divided into Enchytraeids (small worms) and Lumbricidae (earthworms). The former are only a few millimetres long, but may be up to ten times larger than nematode eelworms. They are similar in size to arthropods. Enchytraeids prefer to live in acid litter, and feed on smaller organisms (micro-flora) as well as vegetable litter. Earthworms are more than ten times as large again. They are among the largest soil organisms and consequently their population per unit volume of soil is much less than the others. Their size is partly due to the amount of water carried in their body tissues to allow them to withstand drought. Earthworms thrive in basic, well-aerated soils, and in habitat preference are complementary to the Enchytraeids. They also require a high nitrogen intake for their efforts in digesting organic litter and mixing it with mineral soil. The worm-casts so produced are concentrations of nitrogen, phosphorus, potassium and calcium, valuable stores of plant nutrients which are later attacked by micro-organisms. Earthworms are associated particularly with grassland soils where their cultivating activity contributes to the excellent structural properties of these soils.

Mollusca are slugs and snails, in the same size group as earthworms and complementary to them in choice of habitat. Their food supply is mainly organic litter, and because of the digestive juices they possess, they can decompose material rich in carbonaceous cellulose; they are likely to be numerous in tough, woody, and acid organic materials.

Limiting conditions on the activity of soil organisms. Despite the enormous numbers of micro- and macro-organisms to be found in any unit measure of soil, seldom is there any competition for volume-space among their populations. Such is the size variation among soil organisms—the tenfold increase in size between groups has been stressed—that their use of habitat operates at different levels. Competition for space has to be considered at the appropriate size level of the organism, and then it is rarely a limiting factor on activity. Earthworms and slugs individually require more space than any other of the organisms considered—probably more than 10,000 times as much as one of the micro-flora—but they are only in competition with each other for this kind of space.

More important is a suitable food supply, or substrate, for which there is likely to be competition. Certain types of organic solutions and easily digestible organic litter can support a wide variety of species and groups of soil organism. Some of the micro-flora as well as the protozoa can be the food supply for many larger species of soil fauna. In both cases, the limitation of food resource can become a controlling factor on population size, and is more likely to be a control than lack of moisture. It is true that moisture is essential at some or all stages in the life of a soil organism, but provided it is present in minimal quantity at the outset of decomposition, more will be created by organism activity as 'metabolic water'. Usually sufficient moisture is present in the surface organic litter of humid environments to allow decomposition to continue, but temporary desiccation and a break in activity can occur in the rhizosphere with excessive transpiration.

Soil organisms require space, food, moisture, heat and oxygen. The last is essential for their respiration, and the oxygen intake can become limiting in quantity. The gas is usually in plentiful supply, but can become mixed with carbon dioxide if the latter is present in high proportion in the soil atmosphere. Above the soil surface, carbon dioxide makes up only 0·03 per cent of the atmosphere and its shortage may even become a limiting factor on photosynthesis. Because of carbon dioxide release through the respiration of both roots and organisms, the proportion of the gas in the soil atmosphere can be up to one hundred times greater, or as much as 3 per cent. Soil organism activity is inhibited where the carbon dioxide proportion is at or near this maximum.

Organic soils. The definition and classification of organic soils has been so varied and various that it is impossible to suggest a simple and universally acceptable system. This is perhaps surprising for a type of soil that seems to have clearly visible morphological properties, suitable as classification criteria. Much controversy has surrounded the sub-division of organic soils into different types, and there is frightening confusion over terminology. Perhaps the latter explains the former to some extent.

The classification of peatland (as a landscape unit including organic soils) has a long history, which dates back to the seventeenth century in the case of Ireland. The European approach has been a genetic one, concentrating on the distinction between 'low moor' or 'high moor' forms of lowland peat bog. In the British Isles, these are known as blanket bog and raised bog respectively. Blanket bog is acid peat up to about 3 metres thickness which completely envelops level to gently undulating topography, while raised bogs (high moor) are two-layered formations in which the upper sphagnum moss layer grows up to heights of as much as 8–10 metres above fen peat resting on the mineral floor. Both owe their origin to the wetness of their site which prevents organic decomposition, but site wetness can be produced in several ways. It can be caused by the collection of groundwater in depressions. If the climate is wet enough, this leads ultimately to the formation of raised bogs growing on top of the earlier silt and organic infilling (fen peat). In the initial stage of such a development, the collection of mineral-rich groundwater provides a usually alkaline, base-saturated medium so that the plants in the lowest layers eventually comprise basic or fen peat. The absorbent qualities of the upper sphagnum moss allow it to find nutrients from atmospheric moisture and develop the outer domed surface of a raised bog; it is always acid. In drier climates, the lower peat may exist without a capping layer. Variations also exist in the origins of blanket bog, some being the product of site wetness due to an impermeable mineral soil, and others develop from excessive atmospheric wetness. Lowland blanket peat may belong to either, while upland or hill peat (otherwise called high level blanket peat) is associated with atmospheric or climatic wetness. Hill peat is usually restricted to upland environments with a mean annual precipitation at least three times the evapotranspiration, but in highly oceanic climates it may merge down into lowland blanket peat. This happens, for example, in the west of Ireland, as is shown in Fig 6:1.

On a world scale, the development of peat is due also to conditions which promote site wetness. It is most likely to be found with a mid-latitude humid climate, especially where there is a plentiful supply of organic litter and yet a limited period of temperatures allowing decay. Peat is more likely to develop on level or almost level ground where drainage is impeded. Consequently, the main distribution areas of peat are in the humid climate north-west coastlands of Europe and North America, and extensive levels in northern Canada and central Russia which are partly underlain by permafrost (Fig 6:2). Smaller units of peat also occur in mountains and lowland swamps of the humid tropics.

Where large peat areas have to be mapped, as has happened in Russia and the Canadian Shield, surface vegetation has been used as an indicator of peat type, but difficulties in correlation have arisen. It has been found that the plant species composition on the same type of peat may vary even over a comparatively small distance, for example 100 miles, due to extraneous factors. However, at a more general level, if peat types are being identified by only a few dominant species or perhaps by the quality and morphology of the vegetation, this method provides a means of covering extensive areas especially if aerial photograph interpretation is employed as a technique. The work of N. W. Radforth in Canada in mapping 'organic terrain' for the possible construction

Fig 6:1   Distribution of organic soils in Ireland, including both blanket and basin peat. Although most of these soils would be classified as Histosols, they are so fragmented in distribution that they almost disappear from a generalised soil map of Ireland (see Fig 8:5)

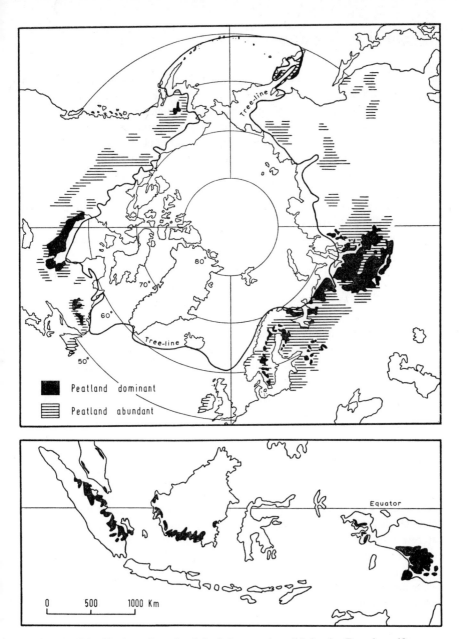

Fig 6:2   Distribution of peatland (mainly organic soils) in the Boreal coniferous forest environment, where most of the world's organic soils are found (after H. Sjörs, 1961). Some of the tropical organic soils (swampy coastal sites) are shown in the lower map. Others are to be found in the great river basins of the tropics

of roads and buildings is a good example. His classification was based simply on the height, woody nature, and growth habit of the vegetation.

In the classification of organic soils, there remains a great temptation to associate them with a type of peatland or surface vegetation as the most easily seen of their formation factors. However, this kind of classification is close to a classification of peatland or bog which is more relevant for ecological than pedological purposes, and is only applicable within one country or defined natural environment. The Canadian classification of 'organic terrain' based on vegetation characteristics would not be applicable in the British Isles. In Europe, pedologists still have a tendency to link organic soils with their origin in a particular bog type, and use surface vegetation as an indicator of properties. Organic soils are sub-divided into blanket bog or raised bog, and further divided by chemical reaction. The most infertile or acid is called dystrophic (Greek *dys* = bad) and identified by the dominance of sphagnum moss. Also acid and infertile is oligotrophic peat which is associated with a lesser proportion of mosses and an equally important proportion of heath plants (*Calluna* and *Erica* spp) and bog cotton sedge (*Eriophorum* spp). Mesotrophic peat is a transitional type supporting a variety of rushes, sedges (*Eriophorum*) and wet site grasses such as *Molinia*. Eutrophic includes fen peat which is basic in reaction. It has a varied species composition including trees like birch, alder, and willow, and a ground vegetation dominated by rushes (*Juncus* spp) sedges and grasses. Fen peat is likely to have reeds (*Phragmites*) and bulrushes (*Typha*).

Agricultural colonisation of peatland, such as took place in Denmark following the Danish–Prussian War 1864–6 as well as in Russia and elsewhere in Western Europe since World War II, has stimulated research and the formulation of concepts on the origin, properties and types of organic soils. From such work the Danish soil biologist, P. E. Müller, in the 1880s, made an outstanding contribution to the classification of surface organic horizons and related soil leaching, which are discussed later in the chapter. Much of the interest in organic soils in recent years has been for the purpose of re-afforestation and consequently classifications have been designed for that specific land use. Whatever the purpose has been, many classifications of organic soils apply to the range of types found within one country and this has frustrated correlation on a world scale.

Organic soils, like any other soils, have morphological, chemical and biological characteristics. The most easily measured such as fibre type and state, degree of decomposition, bulk density, per cent weight content of organic matter or mineral ash, and acidity, can be used as criteria in the classification of organic soils. Most authorities consider that the accumulation of organic matter must be at least 30 cm (12 in) thick to be regarded as an organic soil rather than a horizon. Others, particularly those interested in forest soils, prefer an even deeper minimal measurement of 50 cm (20 in). Arbitrary lower depths are also quoted for the purpose of defining representative profiles—150 cm (60 in) if undrained and 100 cm (40 in) if drained (to allow for shrinkage of peat when dry). Foresters consider an organic soil is shallow unless it is deeper than 100 cm (40 in). At least these depths must be reached if the influence of underlying mineral soil is to be reduced or excluded altogether.

The problem remains of how to classify organic soils. Even the American 7th Approximation is indecisive about the sub-division of its Histosols, and there is still no agreed international classification of organic soils. A recent scheme by Farnham and Finney (1965) proposed a primary sub-division of organic material into three types based on the degree of decomposition (Table 6:2). In order of increasing decomposition, these are fibric, mesic, and sapric types. The system excludes any consideration of the origin of organic soil in a particular type of peatland, and concentrates instead on properties of pedological interest in organic material. The three main types may be sub-divided according to chemical character (base status) and the per cent dry weight content of organic matter. Fibric 'horizons' have the highest content of plant fibres and the best preserved. Because of this, they also have the greatest water-holding capacity (1,000–2,000 per cent dry weight) and lowest weight proportions of inorganic material. They also have low bulk density (volume weight), and usually low pH values and mineral nutrient status. At the other extreme, sapric (Greek *sapros* = rotted) soils or horizons are well decomposed and contain a high proportion by weight of mineral material. They have the highest bulk densities due to this mineral inclusion, and a correspondingly small fibre content and low water-holding capacity. Table 6:2 provides full information on the properties of these three types of organic material. An organic soil may include several 'horizons' of different organic materials, or be

Table 6:2 Probable range of property values of organic horizon types (adapted from Farnham and Finney, 1965)

Horizon type	Organic matter content, per cent dry wt	Fibre content (>70.1 mm) per cent dry wt	Degree of decomposition by sodium pyrophosphate solubility range per cent	Ash content (mineral), per cent dry wt	Water-holding capacity, per cent dry wt	Bulk density (volume weight) g/cm^3	pH
Fibric	70–98	75–95	0·1–0·75	2–10	1,000–2,000	0·05–0·18	2·9–7·5
Mesic	50–90	45–55	0·50–1·5	10–25	500–700	0·20–0·28	4·5–7·5
Sapric	30–50	10–25	0·75–3·5	25–65	150–500	0·30–0·45	4·5–8·0

uniform throughout its thickness. 'Horizon' is wrongly used in this instance to refer to what are really organic accumulations—layers or deposits of distinctive morphological character.

Surface organic horizons. Most soils contain some organic matter, and the most likely place for its accumulation is on the soil surface. Even desert soils contain trace amounts in surface horizons which are the habitat of ephemeral plants and micro-flora. However, the small amount, probably less than 1 per cent by weight, hardly qualifies the surface horizon to be classified as organic. As has been discussed elsewhere, the strict definition of an organic (histic) horizon in the American 7th Approximation classification demands at least 20 per cent organic matter, but in practice much less can affect other soil properties. Organic matter, comprising only 5 per cent by weight, makes a significant contribution by promoting aggregation of soil particles and increasing the cation exchange capacity. Most agricultural soils in a mid-latitude humid environment contain at least 5 per cent organic matter in their surface horizons, and natural soils in the same environment can be expected to contain more. The question still remains, 'At what proportion of contained organic matter should a surface horizon be regarded as organic?' Some authorities have suggested 10 per cent as an arbitrary value, simply because the organic matter becomes clearly visible and morphologically important at this proportion. Obviously this is far short of what is required for a histic horizon, but most surface organic horizons contain little more than this. It is true that they are mixed organo-mineral horizons, but their organic component has become influential in soil modification.

The surface organic horizons of forest soils have been subject to field investigation and classification for almost a century since the pioneer work of P. E. Müller in Denmark. The quality of his research is manifest by the length of time that his findings and empirical classification of surface organic horizons have survived almost without challenge. Müller divided these horizons on the basis of morphological features into two types—*mull* and *mor*. He had worked on Danish heathlands, in beech and oak forests, and found similarities between the surface organic matter of oak and some beech forests and between the heathlands and the rest of the beech forest sites. The former was known as mull humus and the latter as mor humus. He described mull humus as being well-decomposed organic matter, intimately mixed with mineral material at its merging contact. In the gradation zone, there is a strong crumb structure and friable handling properties. Mull humus is also rich in soil organisms, particularly earthworms which conduct the mixing of materials. The original litter of mull humus must be relatively rich in protein, easily decomposed and reflects a high nitrogen and base-rich status in the mineral soil. In fact, mull humus is usually found on almost base-saturated soils, with a plentiful supply of soil nitrate provided by optimal micro-organism activity. On highly basic soils, calcareous mull is found.

Mor humus is associated with different, and in some cases extremely different, micro-environmental conditions. These discourage the activity of all but the acid-tolerant soil organisms. Some fungi, protozoa, springtails, and mites are present, but there is a complete absence of nitrifying bacteria and earthworms. Consequently decomposition tends to be slow, and becomes stratified within the organic horizon. Mor humus is identified by its layered composition; a superficial horizon of fresh litter (L horizon) overlies first the horizon of partial decomposition or fermentation (F), and below that is the H horizon of more advanced decomposition or humification (Fig 6:3). Organic material is not mixed through the mineral, but is superimposed on top of it. The mineral soil is acid or very acid (pH less than 4·5), being particularly deficient in exchangeable bases and nitrates. Plant litter is dominated by tough cellulose compounds, and is derived usually from heath plants and conifers.

These brief descriptions best fit the extreme states of mull and mor. Many gradations exist between these extremes, and indeed mull and mor occur on an overlapping range of environmental conditions. There is no strict divide between the two, and the middle-ground of environmental conditions can produce either mull or mor, or a transitional type of surface humus known as moder or mor-like mull. The term 'moder' (used by Ramann, Kubiena, and others) has been applied in a variety of ways, and it may be best to omit the term altogether from this classification. Mor-like mull has characteristics of both mor and mull. It is stratified into layers of varying degrees of decomposition, but is quite well mixed with mineral soil particles except the clay. It is associated with moderately acid soils (pH 4·5–5·5), being base-deficient but not entirely lacking in nitrates.

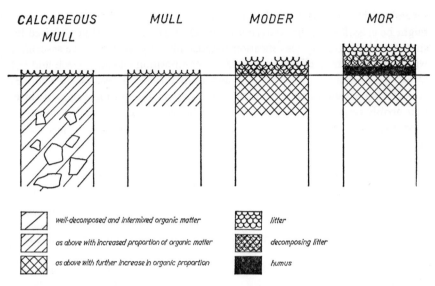

CALCAREOUS MULL   MULL   MODER   MOR

well-decomposed and intermixed organic matter

as above with increased proportion of organic matter

as above with further increase in organic proportion

litter

decomposing litter

humus

Fig 6:3   Mull, mor, and moder surface organic horizons

Table 6:3 lists the probable ranges of property values for the four main types of surface organic horizon. None of these types can be identified by a single property, but only on the basis of a combination of several properties including its associated vegetation and populations of organisms.

Problems arise in trying to correlate surface humus types among different parts of the world. In an area of ancient woodland such as the Appalachians, a wide variety of distinct humus types have been identified due to the complexity of vegetation. It has not been possible to match some types in other parts of the world. Surface organic horizons classified as mor are particularly variable in properties, if only because they can be of variable age. If they are of recent origin or overlying a calcareous parent material, they may be basic, but morphologically classed as mor. A. Burges has questioned the value of laboratory analyses of surface humus to measure field properties for purposes of classification, because of imprecision, and because there is a better correlation between surface humus and its local vegetation. The humus form derives several critical attributes from the composition of the vegetable litter, and might be classified on that criterion alone. Originally, P. E. Müller devised his simple and satisfactory classification because his humus types were associated with a limited range of simple vegetation composition—heath, beech and oak forest. In a classical work on mor and mull formation, W. R. C. Handley (1954) demonstrated that the nature of the organic nitrogen in vegetable litter is probably responsible for the difference between mor and mull humus—at least, more than any other environmental factor. Again he establishes a close relationship between humus form and vegetation type.

Table 6:3   Properties of surface organic horizons

(adapted from P. J. A. Howard in *The Soil Ecosystem*)

Type	pH	C N	Loss of ignition as per cent dry weight	Organic carbon per cent	Per cent base saturation
Calcareous mull	> 7·0	8–12	5–15	40–50	saturated
Mull	> 5·0	10–15	5–25	45–50	20–90
Mor-like mull (moder)	4·0–5·0	12–20	15–35	50–55	10–20
Mor	< 4·5	20–60	30–95	50–60	< 10

The surface humus of grassland and agricultural soils can be expected to have the characteristics of mull or calcareous mull. The cultivated horizon is chemically improved to a high base status so encouraging the activity of soil organisms. The complex and finely divided root systems of pasture and cereal grasses distribute organic matter widely and evenly through the rooting zone. Most of the organic litter of agricultural soils, especially where cultivated vegetation is being cropped above the soil surface, comes from decay of the root system. Whether the organic litter comes from roots or leaves, if the source is a grass or herbaceous plant, the material is easily and quickly decomposed by soil organisms. Earthworms are present to mix the humus through the mineral soil.

Different agricultural crops have their own effect on the humic status of the top soil. It is recognised that permanent or long ley pasture grasses contribute most organic litter and the organic content of their surface horizons is usually about 10 per cent. Frequently cropped grasses and cereal grasses are unable to contribute so much, and root crops least of all. One of the important roles of humus in soil is its contribution to soil structure development and this can be achieved only through some form of mull humus. Agricultural soils, in particular, require this support to withstand repeated cultivation, clay soils demanding the highest proportion of humus for structural stability. For such clay soils, the optimal proportion is about 10 per cent (certainly not less than 8 per cent) organic matter, and consequently pasture grass is frequently chosen as the most suitable crop. Recently (1967 onwards), the traditional grass crop of the clay soils of England has been replaced by economically more profitable cereal crops with resulting damage to soil structure. The organic content of surface horizons has fallen to as low as 3 per cent in some areas, leading to a collapse in soil structure and subsequent compaction of soil.

Mineralisation of organic matter. Man is able to control the chemical fertility of cultivated land by applying appropriate quantities of mineral fertiliser, but under natural conditions fertility and the success of plant growth depend on the conversion of certain nutrients from organic into inorganic compounds. This conversion of elements such as carbon, nitrogen, sulphur, and phosphorus is part of the process of organic decay and is specifically known as the mineralisation of organic matter. *Carbon* is not usually considered an essential element in soil fertility, but is necessary for photosynthesis by plants. The maintenance of a supply of carbon dioxide in the atmosphere for this use is only made possible by release of the gas during decay of organic litter. The quantity of carbon dioxide released from the soil is sometimes taken as a measure of the total activity of soil organisms, but it also includes gas released in the respiration of root systems. Although the total annual intake of carbon dioxide in photosynthesis of plants is only about 3 per cent of the store in the atmosphere, continued intake without any return would reduce the carbon dioxide in the atmosphere in only a few years to a level that would inhibit the vital plant process of photosynthesis.

Nitrogen is by far the most important plant nutrient in soil. It is required by plants in the largest actual amounts of any nutrient, and most of the plant intake is in the form of ammonia or nitrate after mineralisation of organic

M

nitrogen. Nitrogen is present in the soil in a variety of organic compounds such as protein, urea, and nucleic acid, as well as inorganic forms like ammonia, nitrite, and nitrate.

Nitrogen is brought into the soil from the atmosphere in two ways; both involve micro-organisms. The first is mineralisation of organic matter by progressive oxidation of nitrogenous compounds. The second is direct fixation of nitrogen from the atmosphere within or above the soil. For the latter, two different types of micro-organism are responsible. These are:

a free-living bacteria, algae, yeasts and enzymes, and
b symbiotic bacteria living within plant root systems in a mutually beneficial relationship.

The common characteristic of both types is a preference for habitats lacking oxygen. Partly to facilitate their nitrogen intake, they have become fugitives from oxygen. Consequently, areas of nitrogen fixation are to be found on the respiring surfaces of leaves, in waterlogged soils, within plant roots, and in the gut of soil animals.

Nitrogen fixation by free-living micro-organisms is conducted in anaerobic conditions by species of blue-green algae and bacteria of the genus *Clostridium*. They are particularly active in marshy tropical soils, and the algae are of considerable value in improving the nitrogen status of wet rice fields. Nitrogen-fixing algae also flourish on arid soils forming a dense surface mat during periods of rainfall. This benefits the soil both by contributing nitrogen and giving some protection against erosion. In aerobic conditions, fixation of nitrogen tends to be less efficient but is conducted by several species of the genus *Azotobacter*, which prefer intermediate to alkaline soil conditions.

The free-living blue-green algae and some species of bacteria find their energy for nitrogen fixation from the conversion of light energy in their photosynthesis. In contrast, the symbiotic bacteria find a carbohydrate food supply from their host plant and in return provide nitrogen. The bacteria involved are species of the genus *Rhizobium*, living in symbiosis in the roots of leguminous plants. Colonies of micro-organisms develop in the rhizosphere, and multiply even more rapidly into nodule formations once they enter the root system. This highly beneficial method of nitrogen fixation is exploited commercially in the cultivation of leguminous crops like clover, peas, beans, and soya-beans.

It is also significant that so many of nature's pioneer plants are hosts to nitrogen-fixing bacteria and actinomycetes. These include lichens, mountain avens (*Dryas octapetala*) and alder (*Alnus*) in tundra vegetation, birdsfoot trefoil (*Lotus*) and sea buckthorn (*Hippophae rhamnoides*) on sand dunes, and a shrub plant *Ceanothus* on some fire-devastated areas. In periods from about 5 to 30 years, the symbiotic nitrogen fixation in these pioneer plants raises the nitrogen status of the soil remarkably quickly to the levels demanded by succeeding vegetation.

Mineralisation of organic nitrogen starts when bacteria and fungi first invade the tissues of nitrogen-rich organic litter. Many species are involved and make nitrogen available in an inorganic form as excreted ammonia. Organic litter with a carbon/nitrogen ratio over 25:1 is relatively resistant to this type of degradation, and inorganic nitrogenous compounds are not produced by micro-organisms until nitrogen is added to the organic matter, eg, in the form of fertiliser.

While production of ammonia during organic decomposition is a common process made possible by a large number of heterotrophic organisms (dependent on an organic food supply), the further oxidation of nitrogen compounds into nitrites and nitrates is controlled by very few species of autotrophic bacteria (making their own food). Species of the genus *Nitrosomonas* convert ammonium ions to nitrite ions, and species of the genus *Nitrobacter* convert nitrite to nitrate ions. In both cases, these bacteria make available oxygen for oxidation as a by-product of their effort to obtain carbon food material from carbon dioxide and carbonates. The bacteria extract relatively less carbon than the oxygen released. They have optimal activity in well aerated alkaline soils, and become almost inactive below pH 5. This process of nitrification—the mineralisation of nitrogen by oxidation to nitrate—is summarised in the following reactions:

$$\text{(ammonium) } NH_4 + O_2 \rightarrow NO_2 \text{ (nitrite)} + H_2O$$
$$\text{(nitrite) } NO_2 + O_2 \rightarrow NO_3 \text{ (nitrate)}$$

Nitrogen is also lost from the soil by chemical and biological processes. Denitrification takes place when several species of bacteria use the oxygen from nitrate for their respiration, and consequently reverse the process of nitrification. Micro-organisms require nitrogen themselves to build up protein in their body tissues. Excessive demand by soil organisms can immobilise, at least temporarily, nitrogen that would otherwise go to plants.

Phosphorus is another element that is re-cycled through the organic matter of the soil. It is possible to find up to 80 per cent of soil phosphorus stored in the organic matter, the highest proportions being found in high-latitude and organic soils. Some micro-organisms themselves contain a high proportion (up to 2·5 per cent of their dry weight) of phosphorus as they are able to synthesise the organic compounds from inorganic phosphate. Organic phosphorus resists degradation by micro-organisms despite attack by appropriate enzymes. It may be due to some protection given by particularly resistant organic matter. Those organisms, from a wide group of species, that succeed in making the conversion, produce orthophosphate (H_3PO_4) compounds. They can also convert inorganic forms of phosphorus into soluble orthophosphate which is absorbed into plant roots. It is difficult to keep these phosphates in solution as they readily revert back into a fixed and unavailable inorganic state.

Sulphur is available to plants in the sulphate ion, which is another inorganic product of the microbial change of organic matter. Autotrophic bacteria (with the same function as species of *Nitrosomonas* and *Nitrobacter* in the nitrogen cycle) of the genus *Thiobacillus* are most active in acid and anaerobic conditions. Sulphides are produced first and subsequently oxidised into sulphate. There are some heterotrophic bacteria and fungi that achieve the same results in aerobic soils. Under anaerobic conditions, a variety of anaerobic bacteria function as sulphate-reducing organisms in removing oxygen and releasing hydrogen sulphide gas from the sulphate compounds.

The activity of soil organisms is varied, being both beneficial to and competitive with living plants. Some organisms require large quantities of nitrogen and phosphorus, and can render these unavailable to plants. However disadvantageous this may be, it is more than balanced by the constructive role of micro-organisms in the mineralisation of certain elements from organic litter and their maintenance in a solution that can be absorbed by plants. When this function is added to that of soil structure improvement created by soil fauna and humus, it becomes clear that soil fertility is largely a function of biological activity. This is one of the main topics considered in the following chapter—'Soil as a Resource'.

Bibliography

BURGES, ALAN. *Micro-organisms in the soil*, Hutchinson University Library, 1958.

BURGES, A. and RAW, F. *Soil Biology*, Academic Press, 1967.

FARNHAM, R. S. and FINNEY, H. R. Classification and properties of organic soils, *Advances in Agronomy*, 17 (1965), 115–62.

HANDLEY, W. R. C. *Mull and mor formation in relation to forest soils*, Forestry Commission Bulletin, No 23, HMSO, 1954.

JACKSON, RICHARD M. and RAW, FRANK. *Life in the soil*, Studies in Biology No 2, Edward Arnold, 1966.

KÜHNELT, W. (trans Walker, N.). *Soil biology*, Faber and Faber, 1961.

PHILLIPSON, JOHN. *Ecological energetics*, The Institute of Biology's Studies in Biology No 1, Edward Arnold, 1966.

RADFORTH, N. W. Organic terrain, pp 115–46 in *Soils in Canada*, ed R. F. Legget, Toronto, 1965.

SHEALS, J. G. (Ed). *The soil ecosystem*, The Systematics Association, 1969.

SJÖRS, H. Surface patterns in Boreal peatland, *Endeavour*, 20 (1961), 217–24.

WALLWORK, JOHN A. *Ecology of soil animals*, McGraw-Hill, London, 1970.

UNESCO. *Soil Biology*, Reviews of research, 1969.

CHAPTER SEVEN

Soil as a Resource

THE EVALUATION OF SOIL AS A RESOURCE DEPENDS ON THE TIME AND PLACE, AND on its use; a soil can only be assessed within a specific context. It is a resource chiefly for agriculture, but as land it is also used for forestry, industrial, urban, and recreational purposes. Although weathering and pedogenesis also produce materials which are exploited for industrial use, this discussion of soil will be confined to its agricultural exploitation which varies with the place and with the crop, and which has changed over time with improvements in farm organisation and technology. Physical, social, and economic controls on agriculture embrace a number of variables, eg, site, location, labour, capital, etc, each of which may modify the resource value of soil. Thus, it is a relative rather than an actual measure, constrained by a specific set of variables which consequently may be almost unique to a particular situation. Even within one farm of a defined agricultural system at one point in time, a soil is likely to be more favourable, and hence require less treatment and expenditure, for one crop than for another. Soil value will also change with the passage of time, as it can be altered economically by changes in costs of crop production, and physically by repeated cultivation of the same crops in the same fields. Unless rotations are followed to compensate for different crop demands and effects, the physico-chemical condition of the soil—part of its resource value—will deteriorate in time.

The resource value of soil in the agricultural productivity sense, otherwise called soil fertility, is its capacity to produce satisfactory yields of cultivated plants. The potential yield of crops depends ultimately on climate, and where actual yields are short of the potential it is due to limiting soil and site properties, lack of expenditure on changing the improvable soil properties, the farming system, location with respect to markets, or the management, etc. It is often claimed by economists that the socio-economic factors of location, farm organisation and management are far more likely to affect crop productivity than is variation in the physical state of the land. While this is probably true as a generalisation, there remains some doubt about the extent to which soil and site characteristics can influence actual productivity. In a recent study of a part of Northern Ireland (Cruickshank and Armstrong, 1971), it was shown that a selection of eight soil properties explained up to 43 per cent of the variance in gross margin profits on farms where management and other social factors were kept reasonably uniform. This proportion may be exceptionally high due to the method of farm selection, and certainly soil is less significant in an area where management and organisation are variable. It does indicate, however, that soil has an influence and that soil improvement to increase crop productivity is a major cost to the farmer, whether it is paid now or has been at some time in the past. This is a cost that cannot necessarily be afforded by all farmers, even when technology and the materials are available. Soil fertility depends very much on inherited improvements, and on the will and financial ability of the individual farmer to make use of the technology of his time.

It is rash to make generalisations about soil fertility. It is a very broad term and there are so many different frameworks of reference, ie, different agricultural systems under different levels of management in different climates. At the most primitive level, shifting cultivation draws on the natural fertility of soil and plant residues. Crops are harvested for as long as nature will provide at one place, but the farmers in such a system must be mobile and shift their cultivation to achieve higher crop yields. The frequency of the moves will be determined by both physical and chemical properties of the soil, as well as by the demands of particular crops. The system is successful only if the population is small enough to rest the land between moves and so restore soil chemical fertility.

The next, slightly more sophisticated, system, which allows farmers to become sedentary, is fallow or dry farming requiring some of the permanently farmed land to be left out of use each year to conserve nutrients or moisture. By their decision to establish permanent agriculture, farmers have started to pay a price, albeit in a negative way, by apparently losing income from part of their land each year. Although these measures, adopted to increase crop productivity, are usually associated with a very old and primitive level of agriculture, they are still practised extensively today; eg, in the semi-arid mid-west of the USA, they are incorporated in strip farming. Dry farming to conserve soil moisture may last longer than most other systems as improvement of the moisture status of a soil is one of the most expensive soil changes to make. All these systems up to the nineteenth century committed the farmer only to the expense of his own and employed labour; the scale of his farming was limited very largely by the same factor.

Both the scale and productivity of agriculture was revolutionised by new methods and inventions in the late eighteenth and nineteenth century. Agricultural improvements introduced in Western Europe almost two hundred years ago included the enclosure and draining of land, planned rotations of crops, and the extended use of traditional fertilisers like farm manure and marl. Soon afterwards, the manufactured fertiliser industry was established by a farmer in agriculturally conscious Britain (J. B. Lawes in 1842–3) and by the mid-nineteenth century, the greatest single advance (the making of superphosphate) up to the present in the control of soil fertility was being recognised. Artificial fertilisers have made possible intensive farming which, with the help of advanced machinery, weed and pest control, and the breeding of new crop varieties, has raised crop productivity far beyond the wildest expectation of the Malthus period (*c* 1800). Artificial fertilisers used in Europe and North America account for about three-quarters of world manufactured fertiliser consumption, yet most of the world's farmers, and even many in the developed countries, cannot afford to raise production in this way.

Whatever the difference of opinion among farmers and soil scientists about the definition of soil fertility, all agree that it includes site characteristics of the soil surface, and the internal biological, chemical, and physical properties of the soil. At the most primitive levels of shifting cultivation and fallow farming, all four groups of properties present real problems of roughly equal importance. For the Neolithic farmer and medieval peasant in Britain, or for the Indian maize cultivator and pioneer homesteader in North America, the physical obstacles of tree stumps, boulders, and swampy surfaces were avoided or improved only by colossal human effort. As far as the sub-surface of the soil was concerned, they relied on the inherent properties, or at best, only just maintained a level of fertility by natural manuring. Thus, they were simulating nature in seeking fertility mainly through weathering and organic decay. G. V. Jacks (1963) has said that, in nature, soil fertility is a biological phenomenon that owes most to soil fauna in the work they do to create a favourable habitat for themselves and for plants. It is this natural process of the conversion of energy and matter in organic residues, in addition to the weathering of mineral compounds, that supports shifting cultivation for a few years. In farming communities where labour is plentiful, human effort can be used to improve the physical properties of the soil by digging, draining, stone clearing and marling, as well as raising the nutrient status by applying animal manure or sea-weed. In this situation, found universally up to the early nineteenth century, the greatest challenge and the best chance of raising soil fertility lay in the physical improvement of chemically rich soil. Lee and Haughton (1968) have described how highly valued were the soils of the shelly Irish Sea clay till in Co Wexford, Ireland, at this time, because they provided soil after the hand-digging of 'lazy-beds' or cultivation ridges.

In the past century, the criteria for evaluation of soil as a resource have changed. Artificial fertilisers now mean that the chemistry of the soil can be altered relatively easily, though at a cost, but that certain physical properties such as structure, texture, stoniness, and drainage are so expensive to modify that they are regarded as semi-permanent limitations on crop productivity. For example, sandy soils of low base exchange capacity on glacio-fluvial deposits in Europe and North America can be made productive now by heavy annual fertiliser treatment, along with surface watering and irrigation during drought. Controlled irrigation or the lowering of a high water table over a large area requires community co-operation and expenditure, often too difficult and expensive for the additional economic return.

Chemical aspects of soil fertility. The chemical sources and resources of plant nutrients, although only part of the total fertility of soil, are of geographical interest in cases where they are associated with a particular type of soil or some other spatially variable element of the physical environment. Even with land under cultivation where crop removal of nutrients has to be replaced by fertilisers, the amount of the replacement necessary for any one nutrient will vary according to the capacity of the soil to supply it, to retain applied fertiliser, and the nutrient uptake of the particular crop. Although the natural supply of a nutrient from a mineral, organic, or atmospheric source in any one year is usually much less than crop demand, that supply can be important in influencing the choice and amount of artificial fertiliser applied.

Some sixteen chemical elements are known to be essential to cultivated plants, though some only in trace amounts, and additionally iodine, fluorine, cobalt, and selenium are required in the forage of grazing animals. Indeed, all the chemical elements known to be in soil, and there are over a hundred, are useful to plants or animals in some way provided they are available in less than the toxic amount for the element. With increasing pollution of the atmosphere and the use of chemical pesticides and fertilisers, amounts of certain soil chemicals are being increased and so a balanced supply becomes more difficult to achieve. For example, lead, mercury, and arsenic are elements that are useful in minute amounts, but rapidly become injurious to plants, animals, and humans when in slightly larger amounts. However, pollution of the atmosphere in some areas with sulphur dioxide and ammonia can be beneficial for the supply of sulphur and nitrogen to the soil.

Nutrients required by plants are usually divided into three groups according to crop demand for them, namely the major elements of nitrogen, phosphorus and potassium, the secondary elements of sulphur, calcium and magnesium, and lastly all others required in minute or trace amounts.

Nitrogen. Nitrogen is the most important of plant nutrients. It is often said to be in a class of its own, because with sufficient moisture nitrogen more than any other soil nutrient has a positive correlation with crop yield. Unfortunately, it is also one of the most mobile and easily lost nutrients, and because of this, agriculturalists must take particular care to maintain the nitrogen status of the soil. The high probability of annual nitrogen loss means there is very little chance of accumulating nitrogen in long cultivated soils. Like phosphorus and sulphur, a very large proportion of the nitrogen in any soil is contained by its organic matter so that cultivation and crop removal inevitably imply a loss of these valuable plant nutrients. But despite this, about half the nitrogen reserves in a cultivated soil are still in the ploughed horizon, becoming only slowly available to plants.

There is an abundant source of nitrogen as a gas in the atmosphere, of which it comprises 75 per cent by weight and 78 per cent by volume. The other natural sources of soluble nitrogen, such as easily weathered sediments and the seas, contain only about one-tenth the reserves in the atmosphere. Nitrogen occurs also in the structure of primary minerals in rocks, but is not normally available from that source. Once in the soil, it may be used by plants as ammonium (NH_4^+) and nitrate (NO_3^-) ions and it is applied as artificial fertiliser in these forms. As nitrogen is easily fixed into an unavailable form or lost from the soil by leaching of nitrate and by denitrification, cultivated soils should ideally have most of their nitrogen fixed by the clay minerals and organic matter in a non-exchangeable state. Soils that are rich in clay and organic matter have the greatest total reserves of nitrogen and sandy soils are notably deficient. But as soluble forms of nitrogen are released very slowly from these natural stores, and because cereals take up on average only one-third and root crops a half of the applied nitrogen, due mainly to leaching loss, high crop yields are made possible only by liberal and frequent application of relatively cheap nitrogenous fertiliser.

The ways in which nitrogen is changed from a usable into an unavailable state depend on the nature of the soil. Sandy, porous, freely draining soils lose nitrates by leaching; while clay and organically rich soils that are waterlogged and anaerobic provide ideal conditions for denitrifying bacteria and hence loss by denitrification. Because nitrogen is so vital and yet commonly described as a 'fugitive nutrient', great efforts have to be made to improve the efficiency of nitrogenous fertilisers. Because of their greater efficiency and handling advantages, liquid fertilisers are becoming more widely used, currently supplying over a third of the nitrogen used in the United States. In general, there is a world-wide trend towards using highly concentrated fertilisers containing more than 25 per cent nitrogen.

The biological aspect of soil fertility is well demonstrated in the supply of nitrogen to plants (see also nitrogen cycle in Chapter 6, 193–6). Some micro-organisms, including some bacteria and blue-green algae, fix nitrogen directly from the air, the latter role being particularly important in tropical environments, especially that of algae in the water of rice paddy fields. Other bacteria live in a symbiotic relationship with the root systems of many plant species, and form root nodules in leguminous plants. Legumes such as clover and lucerne are included in crop rotations to raise the nitrogen status of the soil. Bacteria are being applied or inoculated into cultivated soils on a large scale in the Soviet Union to encourage the symbiotic fixation of nitrogen by legumes as well as increasing biotic conversion to nitrate.

Phosphorus. Like nitrogen and sulphur, reserves of phosphorus are largely in the organic matter of the soil, frequently about 30 per cent in high latitudes and up to 80 per cent in the tropics. However, reserves of phosphorus are finite, ultimately coming from mineral parent material, and cannot be replenished from the atmosphere. Consequently, when land is cleared for cultivation, much of the phosphorus is lost with the organic matter and the soil is unable to satisfy crop demand. Phosphorus is usually the first nutrient that must be added in fertiliser to attain satisfactory crop yield.

Inorganic phosphorus applied in fertilisers is only slightly soluble in water unless in the form of ammonium phosphate or phosphoric acid. Organic fertilisers rich in phosphorus, such as farm manure, seaweed, bonemeal, and guano, have been in use much longer and generally provide more available phosphorus than the inorganic forms. Experiments have shown that plants take up only about one-quarter of the phosphate applied as inorganic fertiliser in any one year, as most of it becomes fixed in the soil as compounds not directly usable by plants. These are stable and cumulative so that long-fertilised soils are inevitably phosphorus-rich almost regardless of the type of parent material; it is claimed that fertiliser has contributed half the phosphorus currently found in British cultivated soils. For the same reason, former occupation sites can be identified by high amounts of phosphate, especially if bones have been part of the settlement's refuse. Soils in Western Europe with old and deep cultivation horizons, known as 'plaggen soils', are also rich in phosphate as the result of centuries of manuring (see Fig 7:1). G. Cooke (1967) discussed phosphorus residues from long-term (approximately 50 years) fertiliser treatment at Cockle Park (Northumberland) and at Rothamsted, and showed that almost maximum yields of cereals were obtained without further phosphate application while poor yields were taken from previously unfertilised land that received one phosphate dressing. Even more interesting, the phosphate residues survived within the top 23 cm (9 in), the cultivation horizon where fertiliser had been applied, and had not been leached down the profile. This immo-

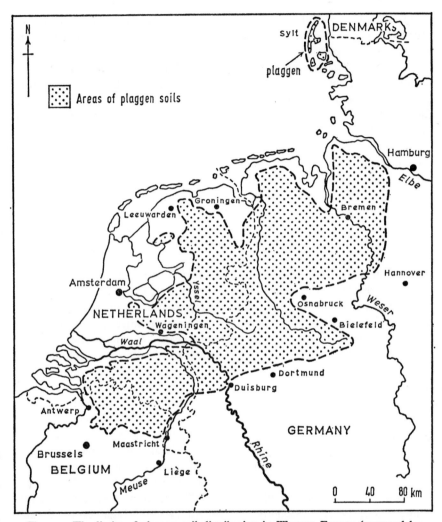

Fig 7:1   The limits of plaggen soil distribution in Western Europe (prepared by
J. C. Pape, Soil Survey Institute, Wageningen, Netherlands). Plaggen soils are sandy
soils that have been fertilised for several centuries with manure, seaweed, and sods.
They have deep Ap horizons, rich in phosphate

bility of applied phosphate, any movement probably being the work of soil organisms, is valuable for archaeologists in tracing buried settlement horizons and past agriculture.

Fixed phosphate is unavailable to plants because it is in compounds insoluble in water or soil acids. This happens when phosphate combines with calcium, iron, aluminium, or the clay complex, so that soils particularly rich in these are often deficient in available phosphorus, eg, deeply weathered, ferralitic soils. The same soils are not usually deficient in total reserves of the element. Phosphorus is available to plants as calcium phosphate at neutral pH; extreme values of pH produce their own phosphorus-blocking conditions. The supply of phosphate to the plant depends also on several other factors including adequate moisture, a high concentration gradient of soluble phosphorus from the soil to the root and the ability of the soil to make phosphorus replacement.

Sulphur. Sulphur is one of the secondary but still essential elements for plant nutrition. Since John Bennett Lawes founded the fertiliser industry at Rothamsted, England, in 1842–3, sulphur has been an important element in mineral fertilisers and particularly in normal superphosphate, the first and until recently the dominant manufactured fertiliser. For over a century since then, there was a sulphur sufficiency for crop production in areas using these conventional fertilisers, but the annually increasing number of cases of sulphur deficiencies reported over the past twenty years has an interesting world distribution. The geography of this decreasing soil nutrient is related to the spatial variation of rainfall, the location of industry, and man's changing use of fossil fuels, fertilisers, and pesticides.

Soil derives its sulphur almost equally from three sources—from the sulphur dioxide of the atmosphere through precipitation, from soil constituents like plant residues, and from fertilisers. Sulphur in the atmosphere, on which the soil is overwhelmingly dependent, is considerably affected by man's activities in siting factories and coal-consuming power stations. Sulphur dioxide is released in the burning of coal, oil, and gas, in the smelting of sulphide ores, and in chemical processes using sulphuric acid. The main natural reserve of sulphides is in the sea; consequently, atmospheric sulphur is high near the sea and around industrial areas. Soils in these localities are sulphur-sufficient with adequate rainfall and crops do not respond to sulphur fertiliser treatment. The sulphur in soil decreases inland, in non-industrial areas, and in arid and high rainfall climates.

Sulphur is lost from the soil by surface run-off, erosion, leaching, and drainage. By contrast with phosphorus, sulphur in the form of sulphate is not fixed in the soil and is a highly mobile salt. Under suitable conditions of soil and climate, more than twice as much sulphur may be lost by leaching as is taken up by a crop in a year. The extreme situation would be that of a sandy, freely draining soil in a high rainfall climate, and there are many such areas trying to produce sulphur-requiring crops. This can only be done by heavy annual applications of sulphur-rich fertilisers like normal superphosphate (13 per cent sulphur), ammonium sulphate (24 per cent sulphur), and basic slag. It is part of the developing problem of soil sulphur deficiency that the use of these fertilisers is declining due to their substitution by more phosphate-rich fertilisers. There is decreasing use also of pesticides containing sulphur.

Sulphur deficiencies have been recorded in some crop producing areas of the southern hemisphere (New Zealand, Australia, South Africa, Brazil, and Argentina) due to a lack of rainfall and a relatively small supply into the atmosphere from the few sulphur dioxide producing industries. The same may be said also of non-industrial parts of the northern hemisphere where supply from the atmosphere is low. There, the problem is further intensified by high leaching losses, especially in parts of Norway, Ireland (see Fig 7:2), and the western coast of North America. The most sulphur-demanding crops (cotton, maize, peanuts, rice, jute, bananas, tea, and coffee) are commonly grown in non-industrial, highly leached areas of the tropics, and so sulphur deficiency is increasingly reported in these areas.

Whitehead (1964) provided values for the sulphur in precipitation in various parts of the world, which range from less than 1 lb per acre per year in remote rural areas of the southern hemisphere to 100 lb per acre per year near industry in Europe and the eastern United States. Whitehead calculated that in general soil must receive at least 10 lb per acre per year from precipitation for the sulphur status of the soil to be adequate for crop production. Below this, fertilisers containing sulphur will be required. The input-output balance is controlled by the several elements of the atmosphere and biosphere which supply sulphur, the crop demand for the element, and the rate of loss from the soil. As these are spatially variable in themselves, their integral becomes an interesting geographical index. Where sulphur deficiencies are found in cultivated soils, the remedy must be found quickly to prevent cumulative deficit. Often a mineral source like gypsum (18 per cent sulphur) is used, and increasingly the new concentrated fertilisers like triple superphosphate and ammonium phosphate carry a coating of sulphur in very fine particles.

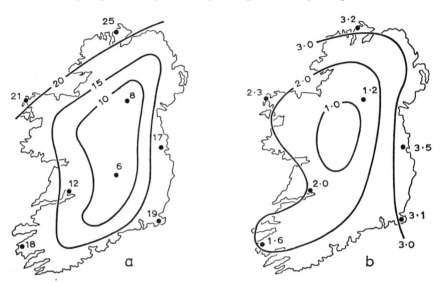

Fig 7:2   (a) Sulphur in Irish soils derived from precipitation, and (b) in rainwater over Ireland. Values are in lb per acre in (a) and in mg per litre in (b). Adapted from 'Sulphur Studies' by P. K. Hanley in *Irish Journal of Agricultural Research*, 8 (1969), 19–27

The cation nutrients. In contrast with nitrogen, phosphorus and sulphur, which are absorbed by plants chiefly as soluble nitrate, phosphate and sulphate salts, there are five nutrients taken up by plants from the soil solution as cations. These are calcium (Ca), potassium (K), magnesium (Mg), ammonium (NH$_4$), and sodium (Na). Calcium, potassium, and magnesium are vital to plants; sodium is required by some plants and desirable in forage crops for animal nutrition. The ammonium ion is one form of nitrogen, which may also be absorbed as a nitrate salt. These five basic cations are attached by electrical charges to the soil colloid, and may be replaced by each other or by hydrogen ions. The nutrient ions in the soil solution are absorbed by plant roots and replaced from the exchangeable cations of the clay-humus colloid, but the soil's capacity to do this is not normally commensurate with the absorption demand of a cultivated crop. The greatest plant requirement from this group of cations is for potassium, while the greatest abundance on the clay-humus colloid is in calcium. But most important of all is the size of the cation 'bin' of a particular soil, or its capacity to hold exchangeable cations. This *cation exchange capacity* varies in size with the clay-humus content of the soil. Clayey or organic soils usually have a large cation exchange capacity or a large potential 'sink' for nutrient cations, and the opposite applies to sandy or weakly organic soils. Agriculturally productive soils require applications of cation-rich fertilisers, but the amount and frequency of application will be determined partly by the soil's capacity to hold cations and the rate at which it can make its own replacement of absorbed cations, eg, sandy soils need annual applications. (See also page 88.)

In mid-latitude agricultural soils, about 60–70 per cent of the cation exchange surface is filled with calcium base ions, 20 per cent by hydrogen, 10 per cent by magnesium, and 5 per cent by potassium and ammonium. The amount of calcium and magnesium taken up by a crop is much less than that of potassium, and all but the most acid soils will be able to satisfy crop demands for calcium for a few years without liming. Exchangeable potassium is likely to be removed by a single crop, and annual fertiliser replacement is necessary to maintain crop yields. Relatively few soils have sufficient potassium coming naturally from their own reserves, and in some cases the total exchangeable potassium falls short of that required by a single crop.

Potassium. Potassium is second only to nitrogen in demand as a plant nutrient in the soil. There are no reserves of potassium in organic matter. The type of clay mineral present determines the soil's ability to replace potassium in the soil solution. Clay minerals of the 1:1 alumina/silica type, like kaolinite, hold all their potassium in the exchangeable form. The release of potassium through the weathering of primary minerals like felspar is very slow, which

N

makes soils derived from acid igneous and many sedimentary rocks deficient in potassium. However, silicates of the mica type like muscovite, illite, and biotite are relatively rich in potassium, and consequently their presence guarantees some protection against potassium deficiency. Thus, soils derived from mica-rich parent material, frequently the case with basic igneous rocks, are the least likely to be deficient in potassium. Like all exchangeable ions, potassium is readily leached from the soil, being displaced by hydrogen ions from acids. Potassium is artificially introduced to soil from mineral fertilisers (potassium chloride and sulphate) and from complex rock salts of potassium, mined only at Stassfurt in Germany, in New Mexico, and in Saskatchewan, Canada. The world use of potassium fertilisers has increased by four times in the past 20 years, and is exceeded now only by nitrogen.

Calcium. Calcium is one of the most abundant plant nutrients in the soil because it is derived from the mineral material of the lithosphere in which there is twice as much calcium as potassium or magnesium. Calcium, in the mineral calcite, occurs in several rocks, all of which have a world-wide distribution so that there are almost everywhere either calcium-rich soil parent materials or limestone rocks available as a local supply of calcium fertiliser. It is fortunate that the supply is plentiful because calcium is also one of the most easily lost nutrients, both as an exchangeable cation and in its mineral source form as a soluble salt of calcium. Even limestone-derived soils in humid climates are usually depleted of calcium in the upper horizons, being composed mainly of residual impurities after the soluble calcium carbonate has been washed out. However, root systems commonly penetrate the lower lime-rich horizons and calcium is returned to the surface through plant remains. Furthermore, there are no fixed or stored forms of calcium of the kind in which some other nutrients may be kept in reserve.

Calcium is usually the dominant exchangeable cation of the soil colloid, so that soil acidity which is a reflection of the degree of saturation of the colloid by hydrogen ions is often nearly an inverse measure of the saturation by calcium, combined with the free calcium ions circulating outside the soil colloid. Calcium is easily removed from the soil, but is easily and cheaply replaced by applied lime. Commonly used fertilisers like superphosphate also contain calcium, but other fertiliser salts like ammonium sulphate displace exchangeable calcium with ammonium cations. Crops like oats, rye, potatoes, millet, and peanuts do not demand high lime status, so will require only infrequent liming. Indeed, limestone and lime-rich soils may never require liming if the land is properly managed.

The advantages of a lime-rich soil are not confined to chemical fertility. Calcium is one of the important elements in structural bonding, and imparts a remarkably strong and durable character to the crumb or blocky structure so desirable in cultivation. Limestone-derived soils are usually well drained. Desirable physical conditions further enhance the fertility of calcium-rich soils; one of the disadvantages is that calcium in particularly large amounts may block the supply of other nutrients to plants.

Magnesium. Magnesium is present in most soils in much smaller measure than calcium, but the plant requirement is commensurately less. In both cases, the natural supply from the mineral source is almost enough to satisfy crop requirements. Magnesium deficiency is common in highly weathered and leached tropical soils, but almost unknown in mid-latitude soils. The exceptions are soils where the deficiency is related to the small size of the clay colloid's cation exchange capacity, such as in sandy soils where there would almost certainly be a related deficiency in calcium. Magnesium losses by leaching displacement of the exchangeable cation and in crop removal are usually minimal compared with soil reserves of the element. The position is altered, however, where (nitrogen) fertiliser salts of exchangeable potassium and ammonium are applied, magnesium losses by displacement increasing by almost as much as the weight of the applied cations. Normally some loss of magnesium can be afforded to increase the soil potassium, but the alternative forms of nitrogen fertiliser are increasingly being preferred in place of potassium and ammonium salts. If potassium is available, plants often reduce their magnesium intake to balance an increased intake of potassium.

Magnesium is commonly found in primary minerals, especially in micas and chlorite, and in secondary clay minerals with the exception of illite. It is also present in useful amounts in farmyard manure and many commonly used fertilisers, as well as in limestone and dolomite. It also comprises 15 per cent of the salts in sea water and can appear in the solid matter in the atmosphere from industrial smoke effluent. In this way, areas near industry and the sea benefit from the atmospheric source of magnesium. Otherwise normal use of farm manure, lime, and fertilisers maintains adequate crop supplies of magnesium in the majority of soils.

Sodium and the trace elements. Sodium is sometimes included with some seventeen or more elements as micro-nutrients or trace elements of the soil. They are either not required or required in minute amounts by plants. Amounts greater than the desired intake by plants can lead to chemical toxicity and even physical deterioration of the soil. It is unusual to have to supplement these elements with fertilisers, but where this has been necessary, it has to be done with great care because an excess may be worse than a deficiency. It is increasingly common to find pollution of the soil by toxic levels of trace-element metals such as manganese, copper, molybdenum, zinc, and lead, accumulating from residues of fungicides or industrial and domestic effluent.

Sodium is found in large amounts only in some soils of arid environments, soils that have recently been reclaimed from the sea floor, or those located near the coast. In Britain and Ireland, as in all islands, soils contain considerable amounts of sodium for which there appears to be little demand from plants. However, there is evidence to suggest that some plants can use sodium instead of potassium if the latter is lacking, and also that sodium can increase the availability of potassium in some soils. At present, little is known about the behaviour of sodium as a plant nutrient and its relationship with other soil constituents.

There is seldom any requirement for and consequently little use of sodium fertilisers. Sodium nitrate is the fertiliser source of sodium, and otherwise it comes into the soil from organic manures and rainfall. Woody plants, most pasture grass crops, beans, onions, flax, and maize are highly sensitive to sodium. A favourable response does come from crops like barley, cotton, sugar beet, turnips, kale, and mangolds, but the explanation is not clear in all cases. Sodium increases the intake of water in root crops which is important in keeping the plant turgid in dry weather. Too much sodium can be harmful to plants and contributes to the structural collapse of the soil, if it displaces the other exchangeable cations to a considerable extent. The soil will be in a state of dispersion, having lost some of its flocculating or bonding elements such as calcium. The condition would be aggravated by the lack of organic matter or the flooding of saline soils, as can happen in the irrigation of arid lands and reclamation of marine deposits.

The problem of maintaining a balance with the other trace elements is most difficult. Trace elements are derived from weathering of rocks, and in unglaciated lands amounts in the soil can be correlated with geological distribution. However, glaciation mixes weathered material so that the minute amounts of trace elements become variable from field to field. The trace element situation is particularly variable in an area like the British Isles which has a complex geology, often with small units of one rock type, and has been glaciated several times. In general, basic igneous rocks are abundant in trace elements and may even have a problem of excess; sedimentary rocks are less rich, and deficiencies usually occur on silica-rich sandstones and on limestone. Extensive areas of sandstone or limestone, into which little foreign material has been carried by glaciation, can be expected to have a sporadic distribution of trace element deficiency. These are usually difficult to delimit areally and to assess quantitatively. Often the first signs of the problem are seen in ailments of grazing animals and frequently the most immediate and convenient remedy is provided by a sheep or cattle 'lick' placed in the field. Corrective measures by fertiliser application may upset the balance in the opposite direction.

Physical aspects of soil fertility. The physical properties of soil, chiefly depth, texture, structure, stoniness and drainage, affect the fertility of any soil. They are now regarded as more difficult and more expensive to change than chemical or biological properties. Improvement of texture and structure on a large scale is not economically possible, and only a degree of improvement is normally possible in soil drainage. Because of these economic as well as practical limitations to improvement, physical properties may be classed as semipermanent, and even permanent in some cases. However, the interdependence of these properties on each other means that an improvement of one will have beneficial effects on the others. Most soil properties are interconnected, and there is a close relationship among the physical group which also includes pore space, moisture holding capacity, stoniness, and even soil temperature.

In the past, various traditional practices were intended to improve the physical state of the soil. In Atlantic Europe, local drainage of cultivated beds was improved by spade digging of ridges, called 'lazy beds' in Ireland. As these were nearly always aligned across the contours, they contributed to soil erosion by channelling surface run-off downslope. In the climatic environment of Western Europe, it took about two to four hundred years to accumulate a bank of eroded top soil against any downslope obstacle such as a wall or a hedge. Raised cultivation beds were freely draining whatever the field drainage below, and crop yield was increased accordingly. Similarly, marl (lime-rich clay) has long been used to raise the lime status and improve the texture and structure of sandy soils in glacial outwash landscapes of East Anglia and elsewhere in north-west Europe. Clayey soils have had their characteristics modified by adding lime to improve aggregation and so improve the natural drainage and tilth of the soil. These methods were reported by Pliny as traditional practices in Britain and Gaul before the coming of the Romans, and they were still used in the same areas up to the early years of this century.

The principles of these ancient cultivation practices are embodied in modern techniques of soil improvement. It is still recognised that clay, calcium, and organic matter should be added to sandy soils to promote structural development with all its ancillary advantages; and that the massive structural clods of clayey soils need to be broken down into strongly bonded small units by exposure to frost and with help from calcium and humus. The main difference is that currently the relatively high cost of these measures prohibits their large-scale employment unless in some intensive cultivation with a suitably high margin of profit. The old-fashioned marling, manuring, and liming of all land that required it, whatever the intensity of farming, came to an end half a century ago in Western Europe when handling costs made it uneconomic.

Control of soil moisture is important for the physical condition of the soil, and involves all the physical properties as well as the external sources of moisture. The passage of time has brought technological developments that make it easier to add water to the soil by surface sprinkling and controlled irrigation. More of the porous soils have been taken into cultivation with a guarantee of harvest, as has happened in some sandy soils of Britain, Germany, and Denmark. Yields, under intensive management, can justify expenditure in these cases, but perhaps less possible is adequate removal of excess moisture by drainage schemes. These are expensive for present agricultural systems, and unfortunately far too much farm land in the British Isles still depends on currently inefficient drainage works installed in the nineteenth century. A recent survey of soil drainage in Ireland (Galvin, 1969), conducted over the period 1964–9 and covering 16,336 schemes, provides interesting information about the causes and cures of drainage problems in that country, and its findings may be taken as representative of the landscapes of glacial deposition in Western Europe. The three major causes of poor drainage in mineral soils were seepage and springs (38·5 per cent), impervious sub-soil (32·5 per cent), and high water table (21·6 per cent). The causes were differently arranged in organic soils for obvious reasons, high water table accounting for almost 60 per cent and impervious sub-soil only 7 per cent.

A more detailed examination of this drainage survey is valuable in providing reasons for the choice of drainage method in particular soils and examples of ways in which soil drainage interacts with other properties. Areas having a deep mantle of clayey glacial till are those where moisture permeability is slowest and where most drainage problems are attributed to impervious sub-soil. The type of drainage for this situation has been shallow tile and mole drainage, ie, the cutting of 'mole-tunnels' through the clayey soil. In cases where the clay content increases to such a level that the related increase of moisture-holding capacity almost prohibits drainage, it is necessary to have closely spaced stone-filled drainage ditches. In low permeability soils, drains nearly always receive a backfill of stones, while in high permeability conditions, top soil and sub soil is used. Tile drainage is the principal method used to improve conditions of high water table seepage and cemented horizons. The last mentioned have to be broken up first by deep ploughing or sub-soiling as no method can bring an improvement while compaction of aggregates and minimal pore space remains.

Good drainage depends on free movement of water through the pore space of a reasonably open, but strongly bonded soil structure. It almost always implies that the aeration and soil surface available to plant roots are satisfactory as well. Root systems cannot penetrate cemented horizons which, in any case, are likely to inhibit drainage and cause the pore space above to be waterlogged. A fertile soil must provide a deep and well aerated rooting zone which has a low bulk or volume density. Organic matter increases the chance of creating a physically fertile soil by strengthening structure, reducing the size of the structural units, and strikingly increasing the moisture-holding capacity of sandy soils. Ploughing also improves the physical state of the soil by disturbing and aerating the top horizons, although there is a danger of a compacted 'plough pan' developing below with repeated cultivation to the same depth.

Agricultural land classification. The basis of agricultural land and land capability classification has long been open to argument. Even the definition of 'land' used in this connotation has been given in a number of ways. However, most are now agreed that it must be wider than the soil itself. Soil is not a complete or independent influence on the agricultural productivity or capability of land; at the most it is only one of a number of physical factors affecting it. When the agricultural value of land is assessed only on its physical characteristics, these include relief, aspect, hydrology and climate in addition to soil properties. The integration of all these groups of factors to produce distinctive areal units of land is complicated, but once done, has the advantage of being a more or less permanent physical classification, which can be used for either land evaluation or land capability mapping. Much less permanent, but equally important, are the non-physical or socio-economic conditions of the land. Agricultural productivity, and hence the current agricultural value of land, is a function of both its physical conditions and man's response to them. All influences must be considered for any agricultural land classification, even if the socio-economic factors are temporary and prone to change with changes in external social and economic organisations. Socio-economic variables include farming structure, farm and field size, fragmentation of farms, level of management, capital investment in equipment, tenure, agricultural subsidies, location with respect to markets, and others. All these factors affect agricultural production, but their influence is not easily mapped.

One practical way to avoid the problems of managing socio-economic data is to select farms where these conditions are uniform, or may be assumed to be uniform. This is done by selecting farms of similar size, organisation, and level of management in a relatively small area, and then basing agricultural land classification only on physical criteria. Although it is recognised that soil properties are only part of the physical basis, soil survey maps depicting areal units of similar soil profiles (soil series) are commonly used in agricultural land classification. The justification given is that soil series are an expression of all the physical factors (relief, parent material, hydrology, and climate) at any site, and therefore provide an index of the local physical environment. While this may be so, it cannot be claimed that agricultural productivity of the land will be influenced by the physical environment of the site in the same way as soil profile development has been. The genesis of a soil cannot be used directly as a measure of its agricultural value. Experimental work has shown that crop production is affected particularly by soil properties like texture, structure, bulk density, depth of free drainage, organic matter, and nutrient status. These are not employed as principal criteria in the field mapping of soil series, even if some may be inferred from mapped characteristics.

Several authors have considered the problem of mapping the physical basis of agricultural land classification. Soil series maps have been used by some national soil survey organisations as qualitative soil suitability maps, sometimes compounding several soil series units if they are judged to have similar potential. Lee and Ryan (1966) working in Ireland considered soil series units to be imprecise and imperfect as agricultural productivity map units, and proposed a subdivision of series units, based on *soil type* (distinguished by texture of the cultivated horizon) and *soil phase* (using properties such as stoniness, salinity, slope, degree of erodibility, etc). This has also been done by the American and Canadian soil surveys in using soil type and soil phase mapping units as the basis of agricultural land capability maps. Work done in Northern Ireland (Cruickshank and Armstrong, 1971) also demonstrated that agriculturally significant soil properties did not necessarily contribute to the distinctiveness of soil series units. The latter were statistically indicated to be significantly different from each other, but partly by genetic characteristics shown to be not influential as limiting factors on agricultural production. The conclusion is that there are disadvantages in using soil series maps for agricultural land classification, and that much remains to be done in testing alternatives.

Land capability mapping, which defines areas of similar physical limitation on the range of potential agricultural use, is usually based on landscape units. A simple scheme, used widely in Britain and North America, divides land into seven classes of decreasing agricultural versatility. Only the first four classes are used for land with arable potential.

Man's impact on soil as a resource. Historically man has a dual role both as an improver and as a destroyer of soil. His activities have created new profile characteristics and modified soil properties of the horizons, changes which have been so extreme and extensive that it seems necessary to find a place for man among the factors responsible for soil formation. A number of solutions have been proposed; these include regarding man as an additional sixth factor of soil formation, or as having his influence channelled through each of the five conventional factors (Bidwell and Hole, 1965). Jenny and other authors have concluded that whenever any of the factors of soil formation change decisively, and man's impact through cultivation is seen in this way, then soil formation makes a new start with a new set of variables. In making use of soil, man operates as a control on the soil-forming factors and initiates a new development sequence. In this sense, the parent material is the old natural soil that is about to be altered by man-directed processes, and a new time scale of artificial soil formation starts with man's cultivation. Previous natural soil genesis is relevant in assessing the nature and cost of reclamation.

Expansion of the cultivated area on the world scale has not been regular in rate as it has been tied to colonisation ventures, advances in technology, and the affluence of the state. State schemes can be part of a planned, long-term economic plan or political design at the cost of other parts of the national economy, for example in cases of large reclamation projects such as the Pontine marshes, the Dutch polders and the Danish heathlands. The maximum area under cultivation or 'cultivated maximum' is not necessarily found at present, but may have been reached at some time in the past. It is usually achieved when a developing society is still dependent on subsistence farming and has not become industrialised to the extent of integrating its agricultural production with that of manufacturing industry. In Ireland, the 'cultivated maximum' was reached in the mid-nineteenth century just before the great potato famine brought the collapse of that agricultural system. On a world scale, the 'cultivated maximum' is the present area being farmed, estimated at about 1·4 billion hectares and being increased annually towards a potential of about twice that area. Although estimates of actual and potential arable land given over the past two hundred years have been in the proportion of 1:2, the ultimate limit of arable land is now in sight.

The results of cultivation practices, beneficial and detrimental, are a change in soil property values from natural to arable soils. The most marked changes are brought about only by massive expenditure of effort and materials, and sustained subsequently by a high level of management. Examples of an exceptional degree of improvement are found in the reclamation of land under water, waterlogged land, and soil excessively depleted of chemical nutrients or physically compacted. In the first two cases, large-scale land drainage must be organised and financed by the whole community. The reclamation of marine deposits, as in the Dutch polders, also involves construction of sea-retaining dykes and a long period of soil preparation before crops can be grown commercially. The basic problem is desalinisation, which is tackled by applying calcium and ammonium compounds to displace exchangeable sodium and by growing early crops that are tolerant of saline conditions, such as kale and most root crops. Related to the removal of sodium from these soils is the promotion of structure, achieved by liming and manuring. Reclamation of sea floor areas is not undertaken unless the material is quite rich in clay to promote soil structure and to retain nutrients. The cultivation of acid and compacted soils is usually part of the expansion of the arable area into marginal uplands in the British Isles. Podsols with acid surface horizons and often compacted but nutrient-rich B horizons require deep ploughing, the destruction of the indurated horizon and mixing of most of the solum before crops can be grown. After that, the soil will probably need considerable and frequent application of lime and other fertilisers for satisfactory crop production in such a high leaching situation.

Long-term and well-managed cultivation is characterised by certain predictable changes in soil property values. Generally, these are as follows:

a a change in pH to about 6·5 if naturally below that value
b a related increase in base saturation to over 70 per cent
c an increase in exchangeable bases like calcium, magnesium, and potassium, although the increase of the last two will not be maintained for long after fertiliser application stops
d the maintenance of surface organic matter by manuring and plant residues, and the consequent promotion of soil structure
e a marked increase in soil nitrogen and phosphorus, the latter surviving long after cultivation is abandoned

f a reduction in bulk density through aeration of the soil by ploughing
g improvement of drainage in the crop rooting zone.

Soil pollution. Man is also a destroyer of soil resources. Repeated ploughing to the same depth encourages the development of a high density compacted
horizon immediately below, known as a 'plough pan'. This causes waterlogging
in the cultivation horizon if it is allowed to persist, and removal requires sub-
soil rotovation or deep ploughing. Soil structure may also be damaged by
physical attack from water and by the tramping of cattle, especially where
there has been a reduction of structural bonding elements. More recently man
is responsible for the increasing incidence of chemical toxicity from excessive
use of fertilisers and pesticides. In particular, the phenomenal increase over
the last thirty years in the application of nitrogen (in Europe and the United
States this has been ten-fold since 1940 and twenty-fold since 1913) has raised
the level of nitrates in food products and domestic water supply far above the
recommended maxima. It is not that the soluble nitrates are harmful in themselves, but they are changed within human intestines to poisonous nitrites and
also reduce the oxygen-carrying capacity of the bloodstream.

Pesticides introduce elements normally present in trace amounts so that toxic
levels can easily be reached. This applies to zinc, copper, boron, molybdenum,
lead, mercury, arsenic, cadmium, and others. Iron is one of the minor or trace
elements as regards plant demand for it, but it is present in such large quantity
that an exceptional increase would be required for a soil to be polluted. However, mercury and molybdenum require a small actual increase to double or
treble the amount present to reach a toxic level; lead lies between these extremes. Lead and cadmium can originate in fertilisers and lime; lead, zinc, and
vanadium also come from industrial fall-out, car exhaust fumes, and insecticide
sprays. The organochlorine pesticides such as DDT, aldrin, and dieldrin are
also soil pollutants, like the metallic elements, as they are not degradable by
micro-organisms and so tend to accumulate in the soil. Consequently, the
danger to stock and to man is often not detected until the accumulation has
passed the toxic level. At this stage, little can be done to solve the problem
quickly and farm land has to be put out of production until the soil can cleanse
itself naturally.

Soil conservation. Erosion of soil by water or wind often means the physical loss of the agriculturally improved part of the soil so that replacement involves improvement of all soil properties. This cumulative cost is so formidable that conservation or protection of the soil from erosion is a prevention much preferable to the cure, and many countries have organisations to promote this objective. Planned soil conservation is a particularly necessary part of cultivation because when the soil surface is exposed, it is most vulnerable to erosion. The rate of soil erosion depends on several factors of the physical environment, particularly on the destructive impact of raindrops on soil aggregates and the scale and velocity of surface run-off. The amount, intensity, and angle of rainfall are critical for surface run-off, but soil can be protected by maintaining a plant cover for as much of the year as possible. Plants intercept rainfall and increase the proportion that is evaporated back into the atmosphere, cereal crops intercepting up to 20 per cent and a woodland canopy 25 per cent of rainfall. Plants also provide a physical obstacle to reduce the velocity of surface run-off, so increasing the time for and amount of infiltration into the soil. Vegetation generally acts as a regulator on the return of water to the atmosphere, its root system and dependent micro-fauna helping to improve the structure of the soil and hence its capacity to receive moisture. Cultivation in arid environments may not allow continuous cropping, and unfortunately soil exposure in dry farming often contributes to wind erosion of the soil. Strip cultivation, practised extensively in the semi-arid USA significantly reduces this risk.

The danger of fluvial erosion is made less by low initial water content in the soil, a permeable soil fabric that will allow infiltration, and by a water-stable soil structure. The last of these can be reinforced by organic matter and other bonding elements. Man can also find ways of reducing the chance of having a saturated soil surface, sometimes by breaking up plough pan horizons which impede moisture infiltration. The layout of planted crops can be arranged so that rows are orientated along contours to reduce the influence of slope as a factor in soil erosion. Contour ploughing and planting can reduce soil loss by half on those slopes up to 10 degrees. This is an example of how a relatively simple improvement of technique, brought about by an advance in the understanding of processes, has benefited agriculture.

Future soil resources. It has been estimated that the projected potentially arable area of the world, assuming the current level of agricultural technology in the United States, is more than double the present actual area of arable land. A recent American Presidential Advisory Committee on world food supply (1967) has shown that 1·8 billion hectares of moderately well-watered soil could be added to the 1·4 billion productive hectares now in arable use, and that over half of the unused potential lies in the tropics. Africa and South America are the continents with the greatest potentially arable area, most of it being in the tropics. This demonstrates one aspect of the under-development of these areas, and nowhere is an understanding of pedogenesis and agricultural technology more necessary. The slow progress in tropical agriculture is linked to that of economic development in general, to absence and inadequacy of transportation, lack of capital, marketing systems, and education in particular. In addition, the physical conditions of the tropics, in climate and soils, present problems for intensive agriculture unless a very high level of management is adopted. Soils of the humid tropics usually have low cation exchange capacities, high phosphate fixation, and massive leaching of plant nutrients. High rainfall is likely to lead to erosion of exposed soil and special care must be taken in the tropics to maintain a complete plant cover, probably practising highly integrated agricultural systems that resemble the natural vegetation. Collectively, Australia, New Zealand, and North America have the possibility of at least doubling their arable area, mainly by extending irrigation. As Europe and Asia have most of their potential arable land in production, future development in these continents must depend on intensification of production towards a fast approaching finite limit.

In the future, greater agricultural production will be required to satisfy world food requirements and this may be achieved either by expanding the arable area or using the existing arable more intensively. In either approach, success will depend on much more than soil conditions. The multitude of individual variables in the main groups of economic, social, political, technological, biological, pedological factors all have the capacity to modify agricultural productivity by being present in critical limiting values. Soil with all its peculiar favourable and unfavourable properties for plant growth is only one among many variables that can limit crop production. Much more will be heard on this problem in coming years.

Bibliography

AVERY, B. W. Soil type and crop performance, *Soils and Fertilizers*, 25 (1962), 341–44.

BIDWELL, O. W. and HOLE, F. D. Man as a factor in soil formation, *Soil Science*, 99 (1965), 65–71.

COLEMAN, R. The importance of sulphur as a plant nutrient in world crop production, *Soil Science*, 101, 4 (1966), 230–39.

COOKE, G. W. *The control of soil fertility*, Crosby Lockwood, 1967.

CRUICKSHANK, J. G. and ARMSTRONG, W. J. Soil and land classification in County Londonderry, *Transactions of the Institute of British Geographers*, 53 (1971), 79–94.

GALVIN, L. F. Land drainage survey II, *Irish Journal of Agricultural Research*, 8 (1969), 1–18.

HANLEY, P. K. and TIERNEY, S. L. Sulphur studies, *Irish Journal of Agriculture Research*, 8 (1969), 19–27.

HILTON, N. An approach to agricultural land classification in Great Britain, *Institute of British Geographers Special Publication*, 1 (1968), 127–42.

JACKS, G. V. The biological nature of soil productivity, *Soils and Fertilizers*, 26 (1963), 147–50.

KELLOGG, C. E. and ORVEDAL, A. C. Potentially arable soils of the world, *Advances in Agronomy*, 21 (1969), 109–70.

LEE, J. and HAUGHTON, J. P. Observations on tax assessment of agricultural land in Wexford County, *Irish Journal of Agricultural Economics and Rural Sociology*, 1, No 2 (1968), 155–64.

PAPE, J. C. Plaggen soils in the Netherlands, *Geoderma*, 4 (1970), 229–55.

RYAN, P. and LEE, J. Soil survey interpretation for crop productivity, *Irish Journal of Agricultural Research*, 5 (1966), 237–48.

WHITEHEAD, D. C. Soil and plant-nutrition aspects of the sulphur cycle, *Soils and Fertilizers*, 27 (1964), 1–8.

YAALON, D. H. and YARON, B. Framework for man-made soil changes—an outline of metapedogenesis, *Soil Science*, 102, No 4 (1966), 272–77.

CHAPTER EIGHT

The Study of Soil—in the Field, in the Laboratory and from Maps

THE STUDY OF SOIL IN THE FIELD AND IN THE LABORATORY IS APPROACHED IN different ways according to the end in view. In a systematic soil survey, which attempts to make an orderly arrangement of information about soils in a given area, soil is inspected at reasonably regularly spaced intervals, and laboratory analysis is concentrated on a manageable number of soil properties. Soil surveys seek to provide basic information about soils for comparative purposes and specifically for their agricultural use. This introductory discussion will be confined to the field and laboratory recording of soil properties of general interest in any type of pedological research.

Soil study in the field is almost always concerned with the vertical surface of the soil profile, and to a much lesser degree with the top horizontal soil surface. The latter is of course important, and is conveniently exposed for inspection where the soil is under cultivation. In such cases, agriculturally significant properties such as organic content, stoniness, and even the state of drainage, can be seen on the surface of the ploughed horizon. However, it is soil profile morphology that is of primary interest in soil field-work, and soil surveys are designed to record the spatial or areal variation of soil profiles.

Soil survey organisations in several countries have tried to standardise the methods of study and terms of soil profile description, and it is advisable that all field workers should follow these conventions. Detailed instruction for soil field-work is given in *Soil Survey Manual* by the Soil Survey Staff, US Dept of Agriculture, 1962 (503 pages), or in *The Study of the Soil in the Field* by G. R. Clarke, 1957 (204 pages) which is the basis of field handbooks published by the Soil Survey of Great Britain. These sources have been consulted in preparing the following sections on soil field work.

Field observation. The starting point for a soil profile description is the recognition of site characteristics relevant to pedogenesis. This provides information on the soil-forming factors at the site, which can be used to assess their probable interaction and hence the genetic soil to be expected. Facts about the site should be recorded on a table (as shown in the example given here) which should include space for field sketches. Apart from the location

Soil site description

Site reference (observer's own system):   Date of sampling:
Map reference of site:
Taxonomic class (or genetic soil type):
Description of locality:
Local relief: Shape of slope:
           Angle of slope:
           Position on slope:
Elevation: Aspect:
Exposure: Recent weather:
Drainage: Locality
        Soil surface:
        Soil profile:
Parent material:
Vegetation and land use:
Climate:

Site and soil profile sketches (entered under this heading)

facts and the investigator's record of the site, information is required about elevation, aspect, degree of exposure, parent material, vegetation and land use, climate, and recent weather. Common sense should guide the observer in what to record. Some of this information will be found on a topographic map, and the rest should be collected easily by simple observation. Slightly more difficult may be the recording of useful data about the relief and drainage of the site. Under relief, one should mention the shape and angle of slope, as well as the position of the site on the slope. The shape of slope may be concave, convex or regular; the angle of slope may be measured in degrees, or placed in one of four

o

categories from level to steep. Drainage should be observed by locality (water-logged to good), surface of the site and profile. The surface will be shedding, normal, or receiving local drainage; the profile drainage way be waterlogged, poor, imperfect or impeded, free, or excessive.

The description of the soil profile itself is arranged by soil layer or horizon. The name and measured thickness of each is given in the first column, and soil property observations are recorded for each horizon from the soil surface to the parent material. The properties selected for field study are those which can be measured visually or by handling the soil. At the outset, it is important to observe the form of the boundary between one horizon and another, ie, whether it is sharp, narrow, or merging; horizontal, undulating, or irregular. The rest of the properties are estimated from the soil between these boundaries.

The field state of wetness for each horizon is recorded in the column for moisture. It may be dry, moist, very moist, wet, or waterlogged. Soil colour is matched with the colour number in the internationally used Munsell Colour Chart, and usually is given for the soil in its field state of wetness. A freshly broken aggregate of soil is taken from the horizon and moved along the 'windows' of the chart until a good match is found. Mottling is an important colour characteristic of gleys, and consequently the percentage cover and colour of any mottles present should be noted.

Soil texture may be estimated in the field by assessing the relative propor-tions of sand, silt, and clay particles present in the sample, although subsequent laboratory analysis is necessary for accurate determination of the texture class. Sand particles, of both coarse and fine sand size, can be detected by feel, sight, and sound; they make a grating noise when rubbed together in a moist sample. The presence of silt particles may be noticed from a characteristic smooth, soapy feel which is only very slightly sticky. Clay is sticky and plastic to touch. It is probably a sufficient challenge for the novice student to judge whether the soil sample has a sandy, silty, or clayey texture, depending on which is esti-mated to be the dominant particle size present. It is important to remember that approximately 50 per cent of the soil sample must be of sand or silt size for the soil to take that textural name, although certain clayey textures (sandy clay loam and clay loam) may have as little as 25 per cent clay (see Fig 2:3).

Stones are larger than 2 mm in diameter, and are recorded by quantity, size, shape, and kind. This is a cumbersome list which may be reduced to quantity and size simply. Shape and kind are implied in the parent material. The quantity of stones may be described as rare, few, common, abundant, and dominant; the size range is from gravel to small, medium, large, and very large stones.

Observations about soil structure recognise both the degree of development as well as the kind of structural unit or ped. The development of structure may be weak, moderate, or strong. There is also a structureless condition in which the soil is either non-coherent and single grain, or coherent and massive. The kinds of structure are based on the shape of the peds. Like texture, these have been discussed in an earlier chapter (Chapter 2, Fig 2:5); the four classes are platy, columnar, blocky, or crumb (spheroidal).

Consistence is the term used to describe the handling behaviour of soil, ie, whether it is plastic, labile, crumbly, or brittle when a clod is broken gently by hand. It refers to the cohesion and stability of the structural units, which is of great practical importance in agriculture. Ideally, consistence measurements should be made at a number of moisture levels, but this is not practicable for most field workers. Because there are different methods and scales of measurement, consistence terminology has become confused. It can be measured on a scale from friable to firm, or from soft to hard. The degree of cementation of soil aggregates should also be included in the description of consistence. It is difficult to assess these qualities, and the beginner in soil field work may be obliged to omit the consistence property, and even porosity.

Porosity is described by examining the minute pores, holes, and fissures through the soil. These should be considered by quantity (rare, few, common, abundant) and a scale of size applied to both the pores and the much larger fissures. Linked with porosity is permeability, the quality which allows water to percolate through the soil. Permeability should be assessed on a relative scale of slow, moderate, rapid, and mentioned under porosity.

Organic matter is a soil property obvious to the observer. Its main qualities of pedological importance are amount, distribution, and degree of decomposition. The amount may be high, moderate, or low; the distribution may be intimately mixed, mixed with mineral matter, or discrete organic matter. Degree of decomposition or humification can be placed on to a 1 to 10 scale depending on the colour of the water that is squeezed out of the organic matter. Raw, non-humified organic matter yields colourless water when squeezed, but the colour of the water becomes progressively darker through yellow-brown to brown hues with increasing humification. The most humified organic matter, which has lost all trace of its original vegetable contents, is a jelly-like, dark brown substance and is almost in the same state in the soil as it is when squeezed by hand. The composition of the soil organic matter is described under roots and fauna. Roots are recorded by quantity, size, and nature. The last aspect is a recognition of woody, fibrous, fleshy, leafy, or root-dominated organic matter. Fauna, especially earthworms, should be recorded if seen or their presence indicated by casts, burrows, or droppings.

Soil properties mentioned so far are part of almost all horizons and soil profiles. There are other less common properties which are part of the soil morphology where they are found. One example is any concentration of pedogenic origin such as a surface efflorescence of salts, a crust, coating, concretion, or nodule, perhaps of clay, humus, or a metallic compound. These are composed of any substance that can be mobilised by soil solutions. There are some simple chemical tests, given on the accompanying tables, which can be employed in the field to establish the chemical nature of these concretions, and in some cases, even the relative amounts present.

Laboratory tests. Some of the field tests just described may be carried out with greater accuracy in the laboratory, often with relatively inexpensive equipment. The test for calcium carbonate is a good example. In the field, testing with dilute hydrochloric acid allows only a crude assessment of carbonate in one of five categories, and for most operators only three will be possible. The test may be adequate if the operator is seeking to establish a zone or horizon of marked carbonate enrichment, but it cannot measure absolute values. For the latter, a carbonate meter (called the Chittick apparatus) is used in the laboratory. This measures carbonate in soil from the amount of carbon dioxide released by treatment with dilute hydrochloric acid. After the dilute acid is dropped on to the soil sample in the reaction flask, the evolved carbon dioxide gas is measured by its displacement of water in one of the tubes of the apparatus. The calcium carbonate required to produce the evolved carbon dioxide gas can be calculated (Dreimanis, 1962).

Table 8:1   Field recognition tests

Colour	Treatment with dilute acid	Treatment with hydrogen peroxide	Hardness	Substance
White	Effervescence	—	—	Carbonate
White	No effervescence	—	—	Sulphate
White	No effervescence	—	Very hard	Silica
Black or dark brown	—	Immediate rapid effervescence in cold	—	Manganese compound
Black or dark brown	—	No or very slight effervescence in cold	Easily crushed by fingers	Carbon
Reddish-brown	—	—	Usually brittle, but may cement particles into hard pan	Iron compounds

Table 8:2   Carbonate testing

Using 10 per cent HCl some indication of the amount of carbonate present can be derived by reference to the following table

Field description	%CaCO₃	Auditory effects	Visible effects
Non-calcareous (less than 0·5%)	0·1	None	None
Very slightly calcareous (0·5–1%)	0·5	Faintly audible, increasing to slightly	None
Slightly calcareous (1–5%)	1·0	Faintly audible, increasing to moderately	Slight effervescence confined to individual grains, just visible
	2·0	Moderately to distinctly audible; heard away from ear	Slightly more general effervescence, visible on close inspection

(continued over)

Field description	$\%CaCO_3$	Auditory effects	Visible effects
Calcareous (5–10%)	5·0	Easily audible	Moderate effervescence, easily visible, bubble to 3 mm diameter
Highly calcareous (more than 10%)	10·0	Easily audible	General strong effervescence, ubiquitous bubbles up to 7 mm diameter. Easily visible

Simple laboratory tests can be carried out to measure some other chemical properties, such as the acidity of the soil, as well as certain organic and physical properties. First, the moisture naturally retained by the field sample may be measured by weighing say 50 g of the field sample and re-weighing after it has been dried out in an oven at 105° C. The difference between the two weights is expressed as the per cent weight moisture of the oven-dry weight. If all the soil samples in a particular survey were collected from a limited area at the same short length of time after rainfall, comparisons may be made among the samples of the per cent weight field moisture which is a close approximation to moisture held at field capacity. A similar test may be done on dry, sieved fine earth by wetting a small sample (about 10 g) and moulding it into a cube or rod shape. The wetting process is continued until the soil cannot absorb more while retaining the shape of the mould. The state of wetness produced should be near to that of the field soil just after water has drained through it. The sample is weighed wet, and re-weighed after drying in an oven. Once again, the per cent moisture is expressed as a proportion of the oven-dry fine earth. Although this test is a subjective one, dependent on the judgement of the operator, reasonably good results can be achieved if the same operator conducts the tests on all the samples of the collection. A soil-drying oven, capable of reaching a heat of 105° C, a precision weighing-balance, and a dry cooling desiccator are required for these moisture tests.

Most laboratory tests have to be done on the fine earth fraction (< 2 mm diameter), so, at an early stage, soil samples collected from the field must be dried and sieved, to remove gravel, stones, roots, etc. The fine earth is used for loss on ignition, which is a measure of the weight loss after heating or burning at high temperatures in a furnace. The weight loss is mainly from the burning of organic matter if the temperature is kept between 400 and 450° C. Above 450° C (and temperatures up to 1,000° C are possible) the loss on ignition will include some moisture from clay minerals, carbon dioxide from carbonate decomposition and even some sulphur dioxide from sulphates. If the ignition is kept at about 400° C for a period of 16 hours, the weight loss may be regarded as a measure of the organic matter present. The loss on solution experiment involves adding dilute hydrochloric acid to about 10 g weighed soil and allowing reaction for about one hour. The same dilute acid is then filtered through the soil, and after washing with distilled water, the soil is dried and reweighed. The loss of weight on solution with dilute hydrochloric acid is an approximate measure of the chemical compounds in the soil sample that could be removed by organic acids in the leaching process.

One laboratory test of interest must be done on a natural clod of soil taken intact from the field site. This is the experiment to measure the proportion of pore space in the field soil, a property of considerable scientific and applied importance. One method uses lamp paraffin (kerosene) to permeate the pore space of the soil clod. The natural clod is weighed first in air, then it is immersed in paraffin and lastly weighed in air again after its pore space is full of paraffin. Using the specific gravity of paraffin, the volume of the whole clod, the volume of the soil plus any retained moisture, and the volume of the pore space may be calculated (Russell and Balcerek, 1944). The same experiment may be done more easily, but less accurately, by packing dry soil aggregates into a calibrated cylinder and measuring the total volume of soil and pore space. Water is then introduced to the soil until all up to the top surface is saturated. At this point, the volume of introduced water is considered equivalent to the volume of pore space. The experiment will not succeed, however, with clay-rich soils which expand on wetting.

Probably the most important and most used laboratory test is that to measure the particle size distribution (mechanical analysis) of a soil sample, particularly from the fine earth (< 2 mm diameter) of the soil. The experiment separates the sand, silt, and clay fractions of the fine earth by successive sedimentation of dispersed particles. The field sample must first be dried, and sieved to isolate the fine earth from gravel and stone-size material. The fine earth is next boiled with hydrogen peroxide (H_2O_2) to oxidise and so remove the organic matter present; the mineral particles remaining are then dispersed from each other by mixing with a sodium-salt solution. Finally, the mineral particles are shaken with water in a litre cylinder, and allowed to settle. According to Stokes' Law and assuming all the particles to be spherical in shape, the settling velocity of the particles is related to their size. Coarse sand particles settle almost immediately, certainly within 3 seconds; fine sand settles in 5 minutes, silt in 2 hours. Only minute clay-size particles remain in suspension in the solution after that. The respective particle size groups form successive layers at the bottom of the cylinder, and their proportions in the soil sample can be calculated from readings taken from a floating 'hydrometer' which measures the specific gravity of the suspension.

Any laboratory manual includes many more soil experiments than are mentioned here, but the majority require the resources of a fully equipped laboratory. The tests used to measure most of the chemical elements, such as nitrogen, phosphate, organic carbon, and the exchangeable bases, are involved, protracted, and demand expensive and sophisticated equipment. They cannot be considered as part of an introduction to pedology, although they are essential in advanced study. They are fully described, along with those mentioned here and various other tests for physical properties, in several well known texts. The most useful are:

American Society of Agronomy (1965). *Methods of soil analysis.*

(Ed) Bear, F. E. (1964). *The chemistry of the soil,* Van Nostrand Reinhold (chapter on methods for chemical analysis of soils—W. J. Hanna, 474–502).

Jackson, M. L. (1958). *Soil Chemical Analysis,* Prentice-Hall.

Piper, C. S. (1950). *Soil and plant analysis,* Adelaide, UP.

Soil mapping. Soil is spatially variable, and for that reason, seems to be a highly mappable phenomenon. Difficulties arise as soon as one starts to look at the nature of the spatial variation. Usually the horizontal or lateral changes in soil morphology are gradual, merging one into another. This makes lateral change difficult to define by a line on a map unless the change coincides with some obvious break in continuity of the physical landscape; then the soil change will also be abrupt. This happens when soil boundaries are controlled by the limits of alluvial plains, rock outcrops, or the breaks-of-slope in hilly areas, but these tend to be minority situations. Soils are highly variable over space, but the type and degree of variation is itself variable and presents the greatest single challenge in the mapping of soil. This problem will be discussed again in a later section, and at this point some guidance will be given for the preparation of a soil map.

However imperfect some soil maps have to be, the making of a soil map can be both an educational and potentially useful exercise. The map being the basic tool of geographers, it is natural for geographers to describe soil distribution in terms of a map. Soil surveyors, who are most often given this responsibility, usually start the exercise in a particular area by carefully considering the variation of the soil-forming factors. Maps of the local solid and drift geology, maps of topography, rainfall, and land use are all examined if they are available. Initial field work is concentrated on a survey of parent material types, climate, drainage conditions, vegetation, and land use variation within the area. By so doing, the surveyor becomes familiar with the local soil-forming environment, or environments if it is sub-divided into several sub-regions. At this stage, it may be possible to draw a generalised sketch map of the soil-forming regions, each with a dominant genetic soil. This is done largely from the surveyor's experience of field pedology, and would not be expected of a beginner. The surveyor is able mentally to integrate soil-forming factor values at any site and predict the probable soil profile. However, this is background preparation, and the soil map is not based on judgement of that kind. Actual digging of soil inspection pits, which is the next stage, is necessary for mapping.

The scale of the published or final soil map is important in deciding the approach and detail in field work adopted by the surveyor. Before digging begins, the scale of the final map, and hence the size of the smallest areal unit that can be shown on it, must be established. The smallest scale likely to be used for the finished soil map would be 1:63,360 or 1:50,000, and the largest scale probably 1:10,000 or 1:2,500 for gardens and farms. Reconnaissance soil maps might be published on a scale of about 1:250,000, but such generalisation is used only in exploratory work. The smallest areal units that can be shown (about 0·25 cm² or 0·5 cm × 0·5 cm) on maps of different scales are listed on the following page.

Map scale	Type of area mapped	Area of smallest map unit
1:250,000	Whole country, province, or state	150 hectares or 375 acres
1:50,000	County or popular map sheet area	6 hectares or 15–16 acres
1:20,000	Drainage basin or development area	1 hectare or 2·5 acres
1:10,000	Forest, plantation, farm, or estate	0·2 hectare or 0·5 acre
1:2,500	Garden, nursery, or field	1·5 m²

In practice, the smallest map units are usually larger than the figures quoted and represent larger areas. If soil information is required for agricultural purposes, and this is its most likely use, detail by individual field is available only from soil maps on a 1:20,000 scale or larger. The popular scale of 1:63,360 or 1:50,000 used for publication by many national soil surveys, is not sufficiently detailed to be of very much use to an individual farmer. The scale of the final map may have to be decided by the cost factor, but the purpose for which the map is being made and the kind of area being mapped should be considered in the decision.

The main objective of soil mapping is to delimit soil units. The ideal, an aim that is never achieved, is that these soil mapping units should be uniform in character, ie, the mapped soil characteristics (horizon properties, profile, parent material, etc) are uniform within the mapped unit. Soil must be inspected by digging small pits of spade-working diameter to whatever depth is required. For example, if the soil map aims to show only surface horizon characteristics, inspection holes may be shallow. Normally, the morphology of the three-dimensional soil mantle down to the parent material is investigated for the soil map, and inspection holes, in a mid- or high latitude landscape, will have to be about 0·75 to 1 metre deep to penetrate all horizons of the solum. Spacing of inspection holes will be related to the minimum size of map unit, and hence the scale of the final map; it is also controlled by the distance from a probable soil unit boundary. Where a change in soil unit is expected or suggested by field evidence, inspection holes must be dug more frequently to establish the boundary as exactly as possible. As these changes are almost always gradual, merging slowly from one distinctive soil to another, so many boundary lines between soil units must be drawn arbitrarily.

On detailed soil maps of a scale 1:5,000 or 1:25,000, sampling inspection holes are usually arranged on a regular, grid-iron plan, with closely-spaced sampling points at intersections—perhaps every 10 m or so. As a general rule, the sampling interval falls within the size of the smallest mapping unit that can be shown on the finished map. The sampling pattern may be regular, random, or free, the last mentioned being dictated by the experienced eye of the soil surveyor.

If the soil map displays map units that are uniform in parent material and soil profile, *soil series* units are being identified. Usually it is possible to show soil series variation adequately on maps of 1:50,000 scale. Greater refinement of soil characteristics being depicted, such as soil type and soil phase, will require the detail of a larger scale. *Soil type* is a sub-division of the soil series based on the texture of the surface soil; it requires at least the scale of 1:20,000 for adequate representation on a map. *Soil phase* is any remarkable variation of the soil series or soil type, usually surface slope, degree of erosion, stoniness, depth, salinity, etc, and can only be shown in detail and with precision on maps of 1:10,000 scale or larger. Special properties of agricultural interest, such as depth of surface humus, depth of free drainage, chemical status, etc, could also be described as soil phases that would be represented accurately only on maps of 1:10,000 or larger scale. However, farmers are not usually able to afford special treatment for parts of a field, and may be satisfied with maps on a 1:20,000 scale that show field-scale variation with some reliability.

The quality and usefulness of soil maps. Any soil map depicting the distribution of genetic soils (such as Fig 8:3) is an expression of the natural environment of that area. On British soil maps, the use of conventional colours for different genetic soils (brown = brown earths, red = podsols, yellow = other freely drained soils, blue and green = gleys, purple = organic soils) makes it easier for the observer to read a soil map and to see it as a representation of the local natural environment. Their value as geographical teaching aids is beyond dispute, particularly as an introduction to the physical geography of an area, but the high cost of production of professionally prepared soil maps can only be justified by a much wider application.

Published soil maps are used in teaching, by government planners for land evaluation, by engineers in road-making and building, by foresters and agriculturalists (see Bartelli *et al*, 1966). Many of these interested parties commission special soil maps to be prepared for their particular purpose as published soil maps usually depict genetic soils. These popular soil maps are usually prepared by government organisations to provide a general inventory of the soil resources of the country. Exploratory or reconnaissance soil survey is particularly applicable in developing countries where very little is known about the soil. Specialist soil surveys follow later.

Most of the developed countries of the world have soil survey organisations and published soil maps of the genetic type on scales between 1:50,000 and 1:125,000. In the United States, the currently published soil reports present the soil map as an overlay on an air photograph on the 1:20,000 scale. These are especially useful for agricultural advisory work. In all countries where soil survey organisations exist, effort has been concentrated on mapping agricultural land first, and even where the scale adopted is too small to make the maps useful to individual farmers, the main benefit that accrues from extensive mapping on a national scale is the collected knowledge about the soils. Success and failure in agricultural production that can be attributed to soil characteristics can be anticipated on similar soils in other areas.

Despite the interest of students, planners, engineers, and builders, it must be recognised that farmers are the main users of soil maps and the quality of soil maps must be judged by that standard. Unfortunately, much of the soil information sought by the farmer is not to be found on published soil maps, most of which are restricted to showing the distribution of genetic soils. Some articles in soil literature make the point that better correlations can be established between crop yield and particular soil properties than between yield and soil mapping units. The exceptions which have been reported are cases where soil property values are almost uniform within soil mapping units. Specialist soil maps which depict spatial changes in properties such as texture and organic matter of the cultivated horizon, depth of free drainage etc are useful in agricultural projects, as has been shown by their success in the Netherlands (see Fig 8:1).

In recent years, several articles in soil literature (Beckett, 1967; Beckett, 1968; Bie and Beckett, 1970; Beckett and Webster, 1971) have analysed the variability within and among soil mapping units. They report that the choice and definition of the soil mapping unit considerably affects the reliability and utility of the soil map; the most vaguely defined units are most

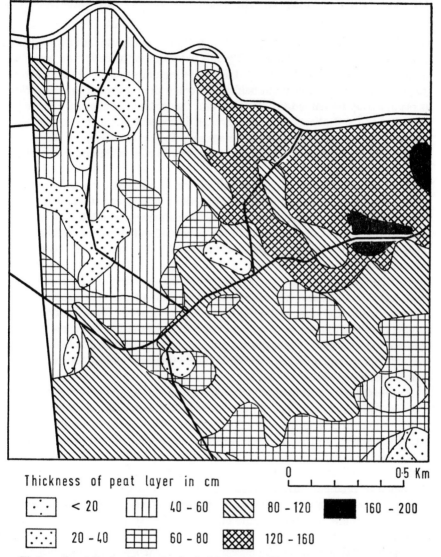

Thickness of peat layer in cm

< 20	40 – 60	80 – 120	160 – 200
20 – 40	60 – 80	120 – 160	

Fig 8:1   Specialised soil mapping in the Netherlands illustrates one possible application of soil survey. This kind of map, showing the depth of surface peat, can assist the farmer in field management. Map after Haans and Westerveld (1970)

reliable within their broad definition, but are not of much use for any purpose. The reliability or purity of a mapping unit decreases as the definition becomes more specific. It is found that soil series mapping units usually are only about 50 per cent pure, ie, only about half the observed sites or area of the soil series is occupied by its named profile class, and the position is about the same in soil type and soil phase units. However, it is conceded that the 50 per cent impurity shown on these soil series maps may not be identifiable or mappable in the field, and may be only minor property variation which does not affect land management.

It has been found also that about half the statistical variance in soil property values eventually measured over a field or series unit is already there within the first square metre. As one would expect, the variance is much less in natural than in man-managed soils because the values of soil properties affected by management, such as the exchangeable bases and NPK, could have a coefficient of variance up to 60 per cent within a single soil series unit. Certain physical properties like texture, moisture-holding capacity, and horizon thickness, considered almost permanent, had less than 10 per cent coefficient of variance within the same soil series units. The same study found that physical property values tend to have an increasing lateral variation down the profile, and are more variable in transported parent materials than in residual. This is not difficult to explain when one thinks of the variation within, for example, a water-borne deposit.

Exercises with soil maps. Soil geography can be taught very well through exercises with soil maps. A soil map can be linked with maps of other relevant distributions in a map interpretation exercise. First, maps of geology, topography, climate, and land use or vegetation are studied and interpreted to integrate the various elements of the soil-forming environment, and then to delimit areas of similar genetic soils. The student should then compare his own reasoned or predicted arrangement of soil regions with mapped units on the soil map. At least it should be possible for the student to show, on his sketch map, soil regions as either parent material or landscape associations of soil series.

It is interesting to know the measured area of the main soil series on a soil map, or perhaps simply the genetic soils or soil profile classes, so that some general information is available for subsequent exercises such as hypothetical planning development of the map area. Actual areas of soil map units may be calculated by using an instrument such as a planimeter, or by counting measured units from squared paper. Alternatively, sampling the soil mapping units at each map grid intersection establishes relative area; on maps of 1:63,360 or 1:50,000 scale, grid intersections at kilometre intervals make suitable recording points. The areas of particular soil mapping units are assumed to be in the same proportion as the number of recorded readings in each case.

Regular sampling at grid intersections may also be employed to measure relationships between soil units and other distributions, particularly of land use. For example, on the Aylesbury soil map, sheet 238, 1:63,360, Soil Survey of England and Wales, woodland remains in an unusually large proportion of the chalk escarpment of the Chiltern Hills and its distribution appears to have a preference for certain soil series (Fig 8:2). To confirm this impression, observations of presence or absence of woodland and soil series should be taken at each kilometre map grid intersection over the non-urban area of the chalk escarpment. When this is done, woodland is found to occur at 1 out of every 4 sites on the escarpment. Of the four soil series involved, woodland occurs with nearly the same frequency (2 out of 7) on the Batcombe series (gleyed brown earth on plateau drift), but with much less frequency (3 and 4 out of 20) on two soil series which are brown earths on chalky head deposits. However, a greater preference for the Winchester series (brown earth on slopes over clay-with-flints) is shown by the fact that woodland occurs at 3 out of every 8 grid intersection sites on this series. Data collected in this way is suitable for further statistical testing by the Chi-squared Test, which compares observed frequencies with expected frequencies based on some assumed hypothesis, such as (in this case) a direct relationship between woodland and soil series areas. This exercise only observes the relationship between woodland distribution and soil series. It does not attempt to explain the relationship as this may lie beyond the evidence available on the soil map.

Using soil maps of non-glaciated areas, the distribution of the mainly residual soils may be compared with that of the underlying geology; a close relationship is to be expected. Next, the student should contrast this with the

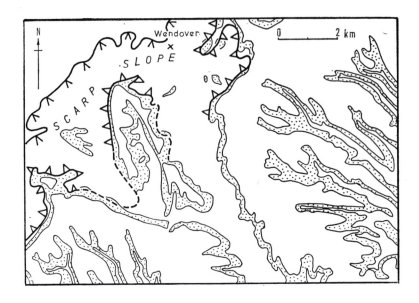

Fig 8:2 The distribution of the Winchester Soil Series (*above*) and woodland (*below*) on the Aylesbury soil map, sheet 238, Soil Survey of England and Wales

relationship between soil parent material and rock type in a glaciated area by superimposing a tracing overlay of one on the other. The general direction of ice movement during the last glaciation may be apparent if the soil surveyor has made careful observation of the composition of the soil parent materials.

The relationship between soil parent material (therefore also soil series) and slope varies slightly according to whether the area has been glaciated or not. Slope deposits, such as colluvium and head deposits, found in positions near the foot of a slope usually form greater accumulations in unglaciated areas, due to a longer formation period. Such an area is the Chiltern chalk escarpment in south-east England that lay periglacial to the Pleistocene ice sheets. On the Aylesbury soil sheet soliflucted head deposits are mapped as extensive areas on lower slopes and adjacent plains or valley floors. The area is one of sedimentary geological structure with only a gentle angle of dip; consequently the residual parent materials and their related soil series are associated with particular positions on the scarp and internal valley slopes of the escarpment. Certainly the occurrence of sedimentary rock strata accentuates the relationship between parent material and position on slope, but the same would hold with any rock formation. Geological divisions within small areas tend to be obscured by the mixing action of glaciation, and parent material becomes relatively uniform along the entire length of a slope. The angle of slope can be measured from a topographic map (by vertical rise over horizontal length), and on some soil maps correlates with state of soil drainage. But this relationship is likely only where there is uniform parent material along the entire slope, whether the area has been glaciated or not. This clino- or topo-sequence of soil profiles has been demonstrated even in a glaciated landscape such as the great drumlin fields of Ireland (Lee and Ryan, 1964). They refer to the slope sequence of soils associated with these drumlins as a clino-sequence because the relationship examined is between soil and slope inclination.

Also requiring uniform parent material along an entire slope is the idealised hydrologic sequence (Glentworth and Dion, 1949), in which the depth of free drainage in soil profiles is progressively reduced towards the foot of the slope (see Chapter 2, Fig 2:1). In this case, soil profile types are associated with position on the slope. Freely draining profiles are associated with the upper break-of-slope and the upper section of the slope; gleying occurs elsewhere.

P

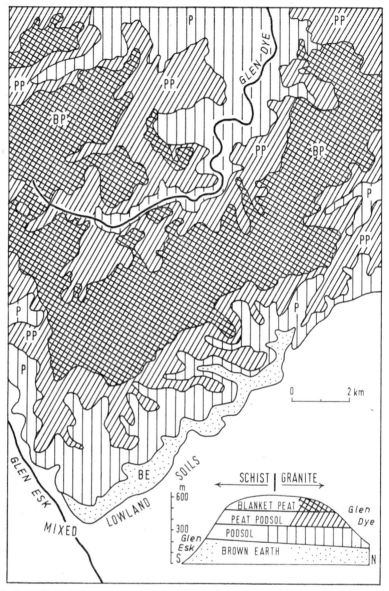

Fig 8:3   Part of the south-east facing slope of the Central Highlands of Scotland, showing the distribution of the main soil profile types (generalised from the soil map of Banchory and Stonehaven, Sheet 66 and 67, Soil Survey of Scotland). The soil distribution is an example of a climosequence; the soil profile relationship with altitude and climate is indicated in the inset diagram

A climo-sequence is the succession of genetic soils associated with changes in altitude (Bryan, 1967). Different soils develop in a predictable sequence, reflecting increasing degrees of leaching with progressive climatic wetness up-slope, but only where the soil parent material of the whole slope is freely draining and so allows the maximum expression of the climatic factor. It embodies in it the transect model of the hydrologic sequence. Climo-sequences are most clearly developed on porous and acid parent materials which themselves encourage leaching; one such case is the south-east facing fault slope of the Central Highlands of Scotland. The parent material is glacial drift derived from schist and granite; it is sandy in texture, acid in reaction and freely draining. Figure 8:3 shows the altitudinal arrangement of the climo-sequence starting with acid brown earths changing into podsols, peaty podsols, and into blanket peat. Using the published soil map of the area (Banchory and Stonehaven, Sheet 66 and 67, Soil Survey of Scotland) students may be asked to calculate the mean elevation and standard deviation of the boundaries between the altitudinal zones of genetic soils. This is done by placing a tracing of the soil boundaries over a topographic map, and recording the elevation of the three main boundaries at kilometre or half-mile intervals. Mean values should be based on at least 20 observations.

Interpretation of some soil map distributions. *England and Scotland.* The division of Scotland and England into soil regions means inevitably that many areally important soils must disappear in the generalisation (Fig 8:4). Eastern Scotland north of the Highland Boundary fault is remarkably well drained because parent material is derived from crystalline rocks and steep slopes are quite common. Even the lowlands of the north-east have podsolised soils. The uplands and mountains present the ideal sequence of progressive podsolisation into blanket peat which has its eastern lower limit at an unusually high elevation. In the central lowlands of Scotland, between and south of Glasgow and Edinburgh, fine-grained Carboniferous sediments provide the matrix of clayey tills and so promote extensive gleying in these lowland soils. Well drained, slightly acid brown earths and brown podsolics are dominant elsewhere on the east and south-east coast lowlands. In the Southern Uplands and the Lake District, as in Wales, the valleys and lower slopes on Silurian shale till develop acid brown earths changing into brown podsolics and even-

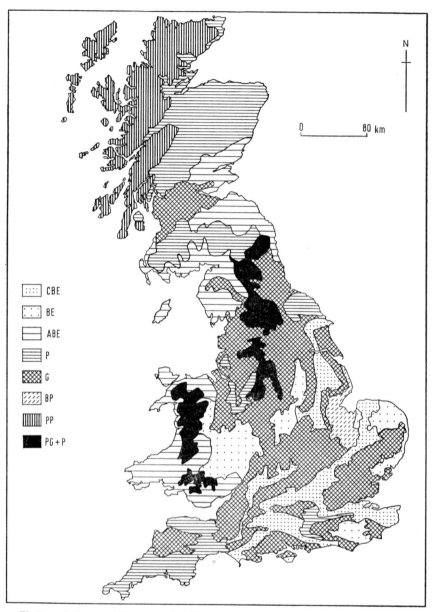

Fig 8:4   Soil map of Great Britain. CBE, calcareous brown earth; BE, brown earth; ABE, acid brown earth; P, podsol; PP, peaty podsol; G, gley; PG + P, peaty gley + blanket peat; BP, basin peat + alluvial gleys

tually podsols with increasing elevation. Gleying, including the formation of peaty gleys, is common on the shale parent materials of these upland areas.

In England, the most striking aspect of the soil distribution is the coincidence of genetic soils with the geological units of sedimentary strata in the east, south-east, and the Midlands. Calcareous brown earths and grey-brown podsolics are found over chalk and limestone, acid brown earths and podsols on coarse sandstones and gleys of some degree on clays, mudstones, and shales. These are the dominant soils of the agricultural lowlands in which parent material can be considered the most influential soil-forming factor. Above the agricultural limit in the Pennine upland, the soil gradation with altitude is from slightly gleyed acid brown earths and podsols into peaty gleys and blanket peat. In the south-west, the lowland soils are mainly brown earths of mixed base status but showing a marked tendency to gleying. Podsols predominate on the Dartmoor granite in the south-west and on other acid igneous outcrops.

Wales. The soil map of Wales (see Fig 8:4) shows several distinct soil regions, even on a small-scale presentation. Above 1,500 ft (450 m) in the western and central upland, the soils are shallow, and either poorly drained gleys or excessively leached podsols. On level and nearly level surfaces, blanket peat occurs, being intermixed with peaty gleys, peaty podsols, and podsols. The soils are the product of an extremely wet environment (above 60 in or 150 cm rainfall per annum) in which the relief and climatic factors are more important than the other soil-forming factors in explaining soil distribution.

On the middle and lower slopes, particularly on the west coast, with less than 50 in or 125 cm annual rainfall, the combination of steep slopes encouraging good drainage and the intermediate to acid reaction of the glacial till promotes the development of acid brown earths and brown podsolics. The soil parent material is derived from Silurian shale and characteristically is yellowish-brown or light-brown in colour and silty in texture. Where slopes are less steep, the composition of the shaley drift encourages gleying and some peaty soils are also found as exceptions within this region.

The third region is the peripheral lowland, usually below 500 ft (150 m) but rising above that height in the drier east, which is dominated by brown earths and their associated gleys. On certain lime-rich parent materials, such as the till derived from limestone on the north and south coasts, calcareous brown

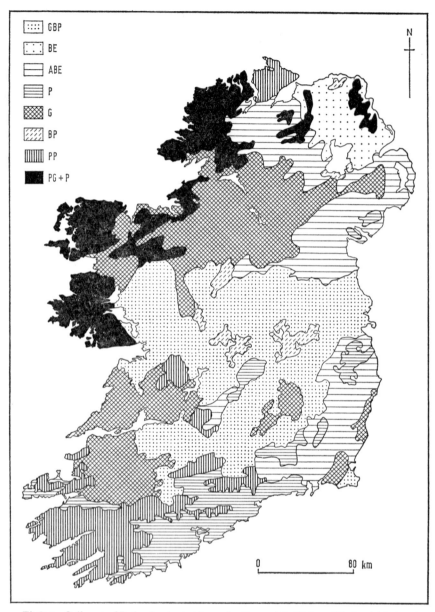

Fig 8:5   Soil map of Ireland, adapted from the General Soil Map of Ireland, National
Soil Survey, Dublin, 1969. GBP, grey-brown podsolic; BE, brown earth; ABE, acid
brown earth; P, podsol; PP, peaty podsol; G, gley; PG + P, peaty gley + blanket
peat; BP, basin peat

earths are found. More commonly, on widespread glacial till of silty or clayey textures, the brown earths are gleyed. A low range of relief contributes to these conditions, and there is a marked local association between soil drainage and slope inclination in the lowland area.

Ireland. Ireland is a country with a complex and varied geology and topography. A classification of its physiography produces a lengthy list of categories and a mosaic of small map units as the framework of the soil distribution pattern. This is particularly true of lowlands below 500 ft (150 m) which comprise 75 per cent of the island's area. Much of the lowland is deeply mantled with glacial till, which is frequently clayey in texture due to its derivation from shales and limestones. Texture of the parent material and the lack of relative relief, for example in the central drumlin belt, contribute to poor land drainage and soil gleying. Although gleyed soils are common and widespread in the central lowlands, they are areally fragmented and mixed with grey-brown podsolics so that it is difficult to map on any but the largest scale. On a generalised soil map (Fig 8:5), lowland gleys comprise about 20 per cent of the total area of Ireland, but detailed mapping would reveal a much larger proportion. Drumlin landscapes are distinctive, and with their wide range of soils cover about 16 per cent of the island. Basin peat, partly intermixed with the drumlins, covers a scattered 2·5 per cent.

The lowlands also have some relatively dry and well-drained soils. Acid brown earths are found with brown podsolics on sandy deposits of granite and shale origin over about 18 per cent of Ireland. Grey-brown podsolics of higher base status are developed on sandy and loam textured drift over limestone on 24 per cent of the total area. Grey-brown podsolics have a close geological association with mainly lower Carboniferous limestone strata in an extensive distribution through the southern and eastern lowlands.

The uplands are divided into blanket peat, peaty gleys, peaty podsols, podsols, and rock outcrop. Blanket peat covers extensive areas in the west (7 per cent over all Ireland) reaching the sea in some places, but terminating at higher altitudes in the eastern uplands. Peaty gleys (5 per cent) are found around blanket peat, particularly in the north-west. The various podsols (14 per cent of total area) are associated with steep slopes of the high granite mountains along the south-west, north-west, and east coasts.

United States. The generalised soil map of the conterminous United States of America shows the distribution of soil orders of the 7th Approximation (Fig 8:6), which must be interpreted both by variation in soil-forming environment and by potential weathering time.

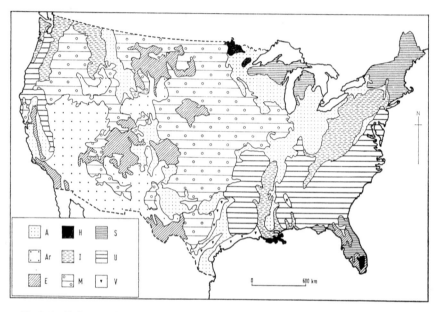

Fig 8:6   Soil map of the conterminous United States of America, showing a generalised distribution of the 7th Approximation soil orders. A = Alfisols, Ar = Aridisols, E = Entisols, H = Histosols, I = Inceptisols, M = Mollisols, S = Spodosols, U = Ultisols, V = Vertisols. Map adapted from publications of Soil Survey Division, US Soil Conservation Service

The most deeply weathered soils are the Ultisols of the south-east and west coast. Lying beyond the southern limits of all glaciations, they have been exposed to favourable, warm and humid, weathering conditions almost continuously for at least a million years. Intense weathering and advanced leaching have produced relatively uniform red, podsolised soils over a variety of parent materials and covering a vast area in the south-eastern States. Coastal areas in the south-east have younger soils dating from inter-glacial phases of the Pleistocene period, and are mainly Spodosols and Entisols.

Alfisols in the Mississippi lowlands have had over 40,000 years development, but to the north and north-east, the youngest leached soils in America—more Alfisols, Inceptisols, and Spodosols—have formed during shorter periods of weathering and pedogenesis since deglaciation. The influence of the present climate, vegetation and parent material largely explains soil profile distribution in these areas. Soil profiles are strongly leached, especially in the extreme north-east, but are shallow and only moderately weathered.

In the high plains of the mid-west, Mollisols areally dominate on calcareous parent materials and where there is a good cover of grass vegetation. Aridity and lack of plant cover explains the presence of Aridisols and Entisols in these western deserts where soil development is a reflection of limited weathering and pedogenesis

Bibliography

BALL, D. F. Soils of Wales, *8th International Congress of Soil Science,* Bucharest, Rumania, V (1964), 69–79.

BAIRD, J. V., BARTELLI, L. J., HEDDLESON, M. R., and KLINGEBIEL, A. A. *Soil surveys and land use planning,* Soil Science Society of America, Madison, Wisconsin, 1966.

BECKETT, P. H. T. Lateral changes in soil variability, *Journal of the Australian Institute of Agricultural Science,* 33 (1967), 172–9.

BECKETT, P. H. T. Method and scale of land resource surveys, in Stewart, G. A. (Ed), *Land Evaluation,* Macmillan, Australia (1968), 51–63.

BECKETT, P. H. T. and WEBSTER, R. Soil variability—a review, *Soils and Fertilizers,* 34 (1971), 1–15.

BIE, S. W. and BECKETT, P. H. T. The costs of soil survey, *Soils and Fertilizers,* 33 (1970), 203–17.

BRYAN, R. Climosequences of soil development in the Peak District of Derbyshire, *The East Midland Geographer,* 4, No 4 (1967), 251–61.

DREIMANIS, A. Quantitative gasometric determination of calcite and dolomite by using the Chittick apparatus, *Journal of Sedimentary Petrology*, 32 (1962), 520–29.

GLENTWORTH, R. and DION, H. G. The association or hydrologic sequence in certain soils of the podzolic zone of north-east Scotland, *Journal of Soil Science*, 1 (1949), 35–49.

HAANS, J. C. F. M. and WESTERVELD, G. J. W. The application of soil survey in the Netherlands, *Geoderma*, 4 (1970), 279–309.

LEE, J. and RYAN, M. A clinosequence of soils associated with drumlin land-scape, *Irish Journal of Agricultural Research*, 3 (1964), 1–12.

RUSSELL, E. W. and BALCEREK, W. The determination of the volume and air space of soil clods, *Journal of Agricultural Science*, 34 (1944), 123–32.

RYAN, P. The soils of Ireland, *Irish Forestry*, XX, No 2 (1963), 2–16.

Authors' Index

Subject Index